Micro Inter

B

by

R. A. Penfold

BERNARD BABANI (publishing) LTD
THE GRAMPIANS
SHEPHERDS BUSH ROAD
LONDON W6 7NF
ENGLAND

PLEASE NOTE

Although every care has been taken with the production of this book to ensure that any projects, designs, modifications and/or programs etc. contained herein, operate in a corrrect and safe manner and also that any components specified are normally available in Great Britain, the Publishers do not accept responsibility in any way for the failure, including fault in design, of any project, design, modification or program to work correctly or to cause damage to any other equipment that it may be connected to or used in conjunction with, or in respect of any other damage or injury that may be so caused, nor do the Publishers accept responsibility in any way for the failure to obtain specified components.

Notice is also given that if equipment that is still under warranty is modified in any way or used or connected with home-built equipment then that warranty may be void.

© 1984 BERNARD BABANI (publishing) LTD

First Published — November 1984
Reprinted — January 1988
Reprinted — November 1990

British Library Cataloguing in Publication Data
Penfold, R. A.
    Micro interfacing circuits.
    Book 2
    1. Microcomputers
    2. Interfaces
    I. Title
    001.64'04   TK7888.3

    ISBN 0 85934 106 2

Printed and Bound in Great Britain by Cox & Wyman Ltd, Reading

Preface

This book is intended to carry on from where BP130: *Micro Interfacing Circuits – Book 1* left off, and where the latter is principally concerned with getting signals into and out of a microcomputer, this publication is primarily about practical applications beyond the parallel or serial interface to the microprocessor. In other words, it is about the so-called "real world" interfacing, including such topics as sound generators, speech synthesisers, motor controllers, temperature sensors, optical sensors, etc. Like the first book this publication does not treat the subject in a purely theoretical manner, or even in a largely theoretical way. Practical circuits using real rather than imaginary devices are provided, together with detailed circuit descriptions and any relevant background information, so that anyone with a reasonable knowledge of electronics should have little difficulty in using these circuits or adapting them slightly where necessary, to suit their particular application. In some cases a near-beginner to electronics should have no real difficulty in using the circuits, but this book is not really intended for beginners.

R. A. Penfold

Contents

IC and Transistor Pin-outs

CHAPTER 1

Audio Interface Circuits

Most home-microcomputers have some form of built-in audio circuit, although this is often in the form of a fairly simple sound generator which just gives a single tone channel, and no variation in the volume of the signal (or envelope shaping as it is usually termed). At the other end of the scale there are computers that have integral multi-channel sound generators which can be used to generate quite sophisticated sound effects and computer music. Some even have the capability of synthesising speech. However, as most home-computers are not in this second category it is quite common for external sound generators and speech synthesisers to be added.

This chapter will, in the main, deal with adding a programmable sound generator or speech synthesiser to a computer, but other audio-related topics such as digitally controlled filters, analogue switches, and amplifiers will be covered.

AY-3-8910 PSG

There are numerous sound generator integrated circuits for use with microprocessor systems, but there is insufficient space available here to give detailed information on more than one of these. The selected device is the AY-3-8910, and this has been chosen as it is reasonably inexpensive, not too difficult to program, is capable of generating a useful range of sound effects as well as music, and it is probably the most widely available programmable sound generator. In fact we will also consider the AY-3-8912 sound generator chip, but this is virtually identical to the AY-3-8910. The sound generator sections of these chips are actually identical, and the only difference between the two devices is that in addition to the sound generator the AY-3-8910 has two 8-bit input/

output ports, whereas the AY-3-8912 has only one.

Figure 1 gives pin-out details for both devices. The sound generator has three tone generators, and these have their outputs available at separate pins. The channels are designated A, B, and C by the chip manufacturer. By having separate outputs it is possible to have a sort of stereo effect, or the three outputs could conceivably be used separately in certain specialised applications (such as for frequency shift keying). However, in most cases the three output signals are just mixed together, and this can be achieved by simply connecting the relevant three pins together.

In addition to the three tone channels there is a noise channel, but an important point to note about this is that it does not have a separate output pin. Instead, it is mixed with one or more of the tone channels, and there is a control register within the device that is used to mix the noise with the desired channel or channels.

The pins marked IOA* and IOB* are the input and output ports. Each 8-bit port must be programmed to have all lines as inputs, or all as outputs, and there are no handshake lines. This to some extent reduces the usefulness of the ports, although they are obviously still adequate for many applications. The outputs latch, incidentally, and inputs have integral pull-up registers.

Clock

There is no built-in clock oscillator, and in some cases it might be possible to use a clock signal from the computer. The maximum clock frequency is 2 MHz and the minimum recommended is 1 MHz. Most 6502- or 6809-based systems should therefore provide a suitable clock signal but with Z80-based systems it would probably be necessary to divide the clock signal by a factor of two or three in order to obtain satisfactory results. If the sound generator is to be used for the production of music the clock frequency could be chosen so that some of the output frequencies coincide with frequencies of the musical scale. This is not essential in that a very large number of output tones are available, and any clock frequency in the 1 MHz to 2 MHz range should provide a

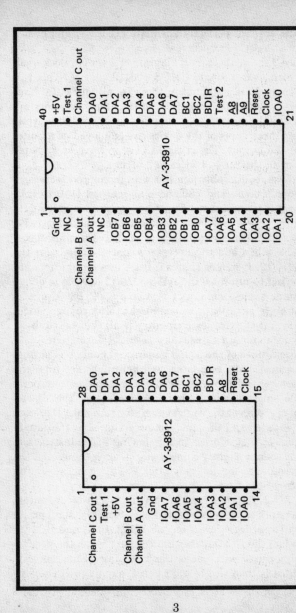

Fig. 1 Pin-out details of the AY-3-8910/12 devices

3

chromatic scale of perfectly adequate accuracy, and over a range of at least a few octaves.

Figure 2 shows the circuit diagram of a simple clock oscillator which uses a single CMOS 4001BE device. This is a quad 2-input NOR gate, but in this case all four gates have their two inputs wired together so that four inverters are produced. IC1a is used as a simple crystal oscillator while the other three gates of the device are employed as a buffer stage at the output. The crystal (X1) can have any desired frequency in the range 1 MHz to 2 MHz.

For those readers only familiar with microprocessors such as the 6502, 6809, and Z80 the pins marked DA0 to DA7 could be a little confusing. These are in fact combined data and address lines, and these give perfect compatibility with some of the GI microprocessors which have a multiplexed data/address bus and the necessary control signals for the AY-3-8910/12. It makes things a little less straightforward when trying to interface the AY-3-8910/12 devices to one of the popular home-computers based on a 6502, 6809, or Z80. It is not quite as difficult as one might think though, and a small amount of extra logic circuitry is all that is required.

In order to obtain satisfactory results the combined data and address lines of the sound generator should be fed from the data bus of the computer, and definitely not from the address bus (which would render the input/output ports unusable amongst other things). Addresses for the sixteen internal registers of the sound generator chip must therefore be sent as data in a POKE instruction, followed by the data to be written to that address in a following POKE instruction. This may seem a slightly clumsy way of doing things, but the driving software for the generator is still generally quite simple to write.

The AY-3-8910/12 chips have four modes of operation, and the required mode is selected by setting the appropriate combination of logic levels on the BDIR, BC1, and BC2 inputs. In fact the BC2 input is unnecessary when the generators are not used with one of the matching GI microprocessors, and it is then tied to the positive supply rail. The four modes of operation plus the corresponding BC1 and BDIR

4

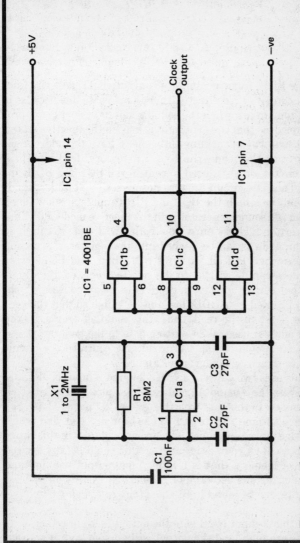

Fig. 2 A clock circuit for the 8910/12 sound generators

logic levels required are listed below:

Function	BDIR	BC1
Inactive	0	0
Read	0	1
Write	1	0
Latch Address	1	1

The BDIR input is almost a conventional read/write line, but it cannot be fed directly from a read/write line because it must remain low when the sound generator is not being programmed (so that the generator is kept in the inactive state). The usual way of tackling things is to have the address decoder (plus the read/write line if necessary) feeding into a gate circuit which is used to control the BC1 and BDIR inputs. This gate circuit must be designed so that under standby conditions both the BC1 and BDIR inputs are low (logic 0), and the sound generator is in the inactive mode. POKEing to a certain address must take both BDIR and BC1 high so that an address can be latched into the generator. A second address when POKEd must set BDIR high and BC1 low so that data can be written to the selected register. Finally, if an input port is to be used, there must be an address which, when PEEKed, sets BDIR low and BC1 high so that the generator is set in the read mode (this could, of course, be the same address used when writing data to the generator).

For a simple example of a suitable control logic circuit refer to the circuit diagram of Figure 3.

This uses two gates of a 74LS02 (quad 2-input NOR gate) to process the A0 and A1 address lines, plus a decoded block of memory. In this case we will assume that page FC (i.e. hex addresses from FC00 to FCFF) has been decoded, and that a negative pulse is provided whenever an address in this range is accessed. Of course, in practice this could be any desired block of memory that is free for input/output use and and does not include decoding of A0 and A1. Details off address decoding can be found in BP130: *Micro Interfacing Circuits – Book 1.*

With a 2-input NOR gate the output is low if either of its inputs are high, and the output will only go high if both in-

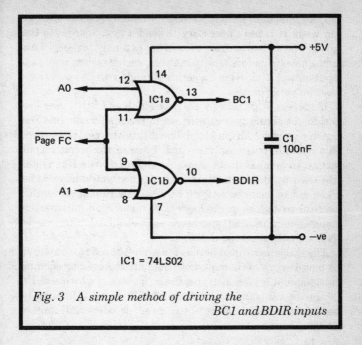

*Fig. 3 A simple method of driving the
BC1 and BDIR inputs*

puts are low. In this case one input of each gate is connected
to the decoded page FC line which is normally high, and the
outputs of both gates are therefore low under stand-by conditions. With both the BC1 and BDIR inputs low this gives the
required inactive state from the 8910/12 sound generator.

When address FC00 is POKEd, all three input lines (A0,
A1, and page FC) will go low, and both the BDIR and BC1 inputs will be taken high. This sets the sound generator in the
latch address mode, and the value POKEd (which should be
from 0 to 15) will select the corresponding register of the
sound generator. POKEing a value to address FC01 sets both
inputs to IC1b high so that the BDIR line goes high, but as
the A0 line is high the output of IC1a (and the BC1 line) remain low. This sets the sound generator to the write mode,
and the value POKEd is sent to whichever register was selected previously. Note that once an address has been latched

7

you can send data to that address (or read from it) as often as you wish. It is only necessary to send a new address to the device when reading from or writing to a new register. This sometimes helps to simplify matters, such as when using an input/output port, where a series of read or write operations must be performed.

If address FC02 is read, BC1 goes high and BDIR goes low so that the sound generator is set to the read mode, and the register at the address last latched into the device is read. This mode is really only needed if one of the input/output ports is to be used as an input. As the read/write line is not processed by the control logic circuit care would have to be taken not to write to address FC02, or additional gating for the read/write line would have to be included, otherwise the sound generator and microprocessor could simultaneously place an output on the data bus.

The system outlined here is for a 6502-based computer, or for one using a 6502-bus-compatible microprocessor such as the 6809, but it demonstrates the basic way in which a 8910/12 can be controlled, and there should be no difficulty in designing (say) a Z80-in/out-mapped decoder and control circuit.

Audio Amplifier

The output of the sound generator can be coupled to a hi-fi amplifier, the sound input of a TV modulator, the audio input of a computer, or something of this nature, but in most cases it will be necessary to drive a small loudspeaker from the unit. The drive available from the sound generator is inadequate to directly drive a loudspeaker properly, but a small power amplifier is sufficient to boost the output to a suitable level. Figure 4 shows a suitable circuit based on a LM386 audio power amplifier IC.

The three outputs of the sound generator chip are simply wired together and connected to a common load resistor (R2). C2 couples the audio output signal to volume control VR1, and from here the signal is fed directly to the non-inverting input of IC1. No DC-blocking capacitor is needed between VR1 and IC1. C3 is a filter capacitor which helps to avoid

8

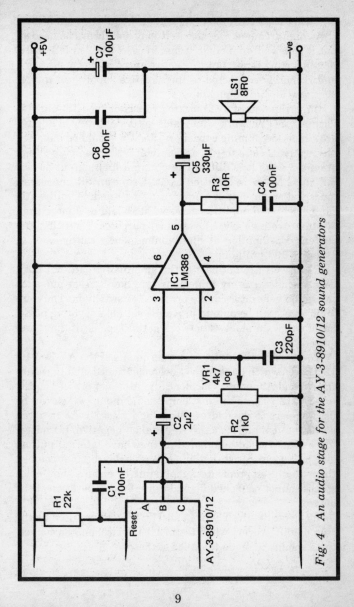

Fig. 4   An audio stage for the AY-3-8910/12 sound generators

problems with stray pick-up of high-frequency signals and stray high-frequency feedback. It may not always be needed, but it is as well to include it just in case. Pin 2 of IC1 is the non-inverting input, but it is not required in this application and is merely connected to the negative supply rail to prevent any unwanted pick-up.

C5 is the output DC-blocking capacitor, and R3 plus C4 form a Zobel network which aids good stability. C6 and C7 are supply-decoupling capacitors, and C6 should be mounted physically as close to IC1 as possible. With a supply voltage of only 5 volts it is difficult to obtain a high output power, but the LM386 is quite efficient. Using an 8R-impedance loudspeaker an output power of a few hundred milliwatts can be achieved, and this gives what should be a more than adequate volume level for normal purposes. Note that the current consumption at high volume levels can be well in excess of 100 milliamps.

R1 and C1 are not part of the amplifier circuit, but have been included merely to demonstrate how a reset pulse for the sound generator can be produced at switch-on. The computer may well be able to provide a suitable negative pulse, but if not, a simple R–C network of this type is all that is required.

There are actually two more terminals of the AY-3-8910/12 devices which have not yet been mentioned, and these are the A8 and A9 inputs. (Incidentally, A9 is not present on the AY-3-8912.) These are just chip-enable inputs which can be used as part of the address decoding if desired. A8 is taken positive to enable the chip; A9 is taken negative. If unused, these inputs could be ignored as they have internal pull-up and pull-down resistors, but it is probably best to connect them to the appropriate supply rail to ensure that noise spikes cannot be picked up and cause faulty operation of the device.

Incidentally, the TEST 1 and TEST 2 pins are used by the chip manufacturers when testing the device, and no connections should be made to either of these.

Registers

With a complex integrated circuit such as the AY-3-8910 or AY-3-8912 getting the right control signals for the device is only half the battle: it must be programmed properly if it is to do anything useful! When adding a sound generator to a computer there is obviously no supporting software in the computer to make life easier. As mentioned earlier, there are sixteen registers, and a basic understanding of these is essential in order to produce music or sound effects.

Registers 0 and 1 operate together and are used to set the frequency of channel A. The eight least-significant bits are sent to register 0 and the four most-significant bits are sent to register 1. Note that it is bits 0 to 3 of register 1 that are used, and its four most-significant bits are irrelevant. The output frequency is equal to the clock frequency divided by sixteen, and then further divided by the number written to the tone-control registers. Thus, the higher the number written to the tone-control registers, the lower the output frequency. If (say) a frequency of 1 kHz was required, and the clock frequency was 1 MHz, a total division rate of 1000 would be needed. With a division of sixteen provided by a pre-scaler in the sound generator, the tone registers must provide a further division by 62.5 (1000/16 = 62.5).

This is obviously impossible since the registers can only provide division by a whole number, but a division rate of 62 or 63 will give an error of well under 1% and should be good enough for practical purposes. Therefore, 62 or 63 would be written to register 0, and 0 would be written to register 1.

Things are a little less straightforward for higher division rates where a number of greater than zero must be written to register 1. The best way to tackle this is to first convert the number into binary form. For example, if the number is 625, this is 1001110001 in binary. The eight least-significant bits are 01110001, which is 113 in decimal, and this is the value sent to register 0. This leaves just the 1 in the 512's column, and 512 is the value that is written to register 1.

In practice, if you wish to program music it is a matter of calculating the division rates to give the required notes, then calculating the numbers that must be written to registers 0 and 1 to produce these notes, and finally putting the results into a table for easy reference when programming the sound generator. The list of notes and frequencies given below should be helpful. This is only for one octave, but as a doubling of frequency raises a note by one octave it is not difficult to calculate the frequencies for other octaves.

A	220 Hz	D#	311.1 Hz
A#	233.3 Hz	E	329.63 Hz
B	246.94 Hz	F	349.23 Hz
Middle C	261.63 Hz	F#	370 Hz
C#	277.2 Hz	G	392 Hz
D	293.66 Hz	G#	415.3 Hz

Things are much easier when producing sound effects since precise frequencies are not likely to be of any importance. A little trial and error is usually all that is needed in order to home-in on the desired effect.

Registers 2 and 3 operate in exactly the same manner as registers 0 and 1, but it is the frequency of channel B that is controlled by these. Similarly, registers 4 and 5 control the frequency of channel C.

The noise pitch is controlled by register 6, but note that only the 5 least-significant bits of this are used, and the value POKEd to this register should therefore be in the range 0 to 31. The higher the value sent, the lower the pitch of the noise. The noise is actually a sort of random-length pulse signal, and there are strong harmonics on the signal when a low pitch is selected. This always gives a strong high-frequency content on the output, and a low pitch value does not give a sound like filtered white sound. This rough low-frequency noise is quite useful for many sound effects though. A high pitch value gives what is a reasonable approximation of white noise. The noise generator is most useful for sound effects such as gunshots, explosions, and engine noises.

Register 7 is the enable register, and it selects the signal sources that will be coupled through to the outputs. An important point to bear in mind is that setting a bit of this register low enables the corresponding signal source, and it is not, as one might expect, setting a bit high that enables a a signal source.

Bits 0, 1, and 2 respectively control channels A, B, and C. Bits 3 to 5 control the noise generator, and enable the noise to be mixed with channels A, B, and C respectively. This register also controls the data direction of the input/output ports. Bit 6 controls port A while bit 7 controls port B. Setting one of these bits high sets the corresponding port as an output (and the ports are therefore initially set as inputs when the device is reset at switch-on). Of course, in the case of the AY-3-8912 there is no port B, and bit 7 of this register is unused.

The purpose of register 8 is to control the volume of channel A, but only the 4 least significant bits are used. The volume value written to this register should therefore be in the range 0 to 15, with 0 switching off channel A and 15 giving maximum volume. If bit 4 is set to 1 the volume is no longer controlled by bits 0 to 3, but is instead controlled by the built-in envelope shaper. The 3 most significant bits are not used.

Registers 9 to 10 operate in the same way as register 8, but they control channels B and C.

The envelope duration is controlled by registers 11 and 12, and register 11 holds the least- significant bits of the 16-bit control number. The clock frequency is divided by 256, and then by the number written to registers 11 and 12. This gives a very wide range of envelope durations. For instance, with a 1 MHz clock the minimum duration is only a fraction of a millisecond, but the maximum envelope period is in the region of 20 seconds.

There are a number of pre-programmed envelope shapes, and register 13 is used to select whichever of these is required. Only the 4 least-significant bits are used. The envelopes available are shown in Figure 5, and this gives the decimal value that must be written to register 13 in order to obtain each of these. Note that where a steady rise or fall in volume is shown, the volume actually rises or falls in just sixteen steps. This stepping up and down in volume is often clearly audible. The first of these envelopes is useful for both music and many percussive-type sound effects (the fourth en-

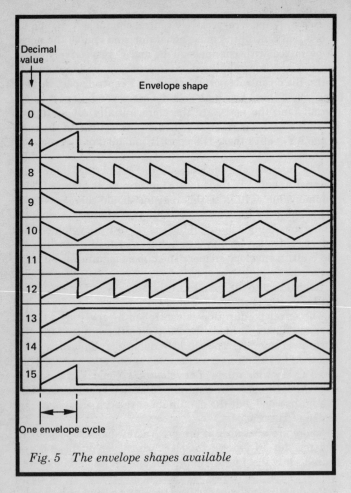

Fig. 5 The envelope shapes available

velope in the list actually has the same characteristics as the first one, and there are only seven different envelopes obtainable).

Registers 14 and 15 are not part of the sound generator circuit, but are the registers used when reading from or writing to one of the input/output ports. Register 14 is used in

14

conjunction with port A, and register 15 is used in conjunction with port B. Of course, register 15 is not implemented in the AY-3-8912 which does not have port B.

When programming the sound generator Figure 6 should prove helpful as it provides a quick reference guide to what

Reg- ister	Function	Bit							
		7	6	5	4	3	2	1	0
0	Channel A pitch	8 Bit fine tune							
1						4 Bit coarse tune			
2	Channel B pitch	8 Bit fine tune							
3						4 Bit coarse tune			
4	Channel C pitch	8 Bit fine tune							
5						4 Bit coarse tune			
6	Noise pitch				5 Bit pitch control				
7	Enable	I/O		Pitch			Tone		
		B	A	C	B	A	C	B	A
8	Channel A volume				Env	4 Bit volume control			
9	Channel B volume				Env	4 Bit volume control			
10	Channel C volume				Env	4 Bit volume control			
11	Envelope duration	8 Bit fine							
12		8 Bit coarse							
13	Envelope shape					4 Bit control			
14	I/O port A	8 Bit parallel port							
15	I/O port B	8 Bit parallel port							

Fig. 6   The functions of the 16 registers

register does what. It is possible to experiment with the sound generator to some extent in the command mode, but in some cases (especially when using the envelope generator) it will not operate properly unless it is controlled by a program so that a rapid sequence of instructions are provided. One omission from the generator (which is common to most other devices of this type) is that there is no built-in control of the sound duration. This has to be handled by a software loop, or perhaps using the timer facility of the computer.

The following program demonstrates the basic way in which the sound generator is programmed. It simply produces a short burst of tone from channel C.

```
10 POKE FC00,4
20 POKE FC01,127
30 POKE FC00,5
40 POKE FC01,1
50 POKE FC00,7
60 POKE FC01,251
70 POKE FC00,10
80 POKE FC01,15
90 FOR A = 1 TO 200
100 NEXT A
110 POKE FC01,0
120 STOP
```

The POKE instructions are in pairs, with the first one selecting the required register and the following one writing the appropriate value to that register. The first four POKEs set the pitch of the channel C tone generator, and the specified values give a middle audio frequency. Lines 50 and 60 enable channel C, but not the noise or other tone channels. The final two POKEs set channel C at maximum volume. The FOR .... NEXT loop is simply to provide a delay (of typically just under a second) before line 110 switches off the tone generator. If the computer has a PAUSE, TIMER, or similar function, it would probably be more convenient to use this to set the tone duration, rather than this system of using a timing loop.

Of course, the addresses used here are for example only,

and in practice would almost certainly be different.

The next program demonstrates the use of the envelope generator. The first six lines again set the pitch of channel C, and enable the channel C tone generator. Lines 70 and 80 set the channel C volume at a value of 16, which hands over control to the envelope shaper. The next four lines set the envelope period, and finally, lines 130 and 140 set the envelope shape. When run this gives a burst of tone about one second or so in duration. The selected envelope shape gives an instant rise to full volume followed by a gradual decay. An important point to keep in mind is that when a repeating envelope is used, or one that holds the signal at maximum volume at the end, the output will continue indefinitely. The volume figure for the channel concerned should be set at zero to cut off the signal at the appropriate time.

```
10 POKE FC00,4
20 POKE FC01,127
30 POKE FC00,5
40 POKE FC01,1
50 POKE FC00,7
60 POKE FC01,251
70 POKE FC00,10
80 POKE FC01,16
90 POKE FC00,11
100 POKE FC01,0
110 POKE FC00,12
120 POKE FC01,20
130 POKE FC00,13
140 POKE FC01,9
```

The next program uses the noise source and envelope shaper to give an explosion sound.

```
10 POKE FC00,6
20 POKE FC01,31
30 POKE FC00,7
40 POKE FC01,223
50 POKE FC00,10
```

```
60 POKE FC01,16
70 POKE FC00,11
80 POKE FC01,0
90 POKE FC00,12
100 POKE FC01,20
110 POKE FC00,13
120 POKE FC01,9
```

The first two lines set the noise pitch value at 31, which gives minimum pitch. Lines 20 and 30 enable the noise (which is mixed into channel C), while the next two lines hand control of the volume over to the envelope shaper. The rest of the program sets the envelope period and type. Using a higher noise pitch value and a shorter envelope period would give a gunshot sound.

The input and output ports are quite easy to use. For example, to write 127 to port A it would first be necessary to set port A as an output. To do this 64 would be written to register 7. Then 127 would be written to register 14. This gives the following program:

```
10 POKE FC00,7
20 POKE FC01,64
30 POKE FC00,14
40 POKE FC01,127
```

When using any device of this type it is really a matter of experimenting with it for a while until it has been fully mastered. The main points to watch are to make sure that a register is selected before data is written to it, and that values written are within the limits of the register as many do not use the full 8 bits. Writing an illegal quantity to a register will not cause the sound generator to crash, but it is unlikely to give precisely the effect you wanted either.

Speech Synthesis

Until quite recently speech synthesis was something that was only a viable proposition for quite large computer systems, due to the large amount of memory required to store even a basic vocabulary in digital form. A great deal of research has gone into more economic ways of storing digital speech, and these days it is possible to add speech synthesis to even a very small and basic computer system.

There are several integrated circuits for use in speech synthesis systems currently available, and most of these have a vocabulary of about 200 words. A device which has become very popular with home-constructors is the SPO256 which uses a different system. It has a vocabulary of 64 allophones, or basic speech sounds. Several of these sounds are strung together to produce individual words, and the advantage of this system is that it gives an unlimited vocabulary since a reasonable representation of any English word can be produced. The required allophones are selected under software control, and only a few bytes of memory are required for each word. Thus, even a computer with as little as 1 k of memory could store a few short phrases without seriously depleting the memory. The disadvantage of the allophone method of speech systhesis is that it gives a speech quality which is not quite as good as most whole-word systems. It is also a little more difficult and time consuming to put together the desired phrases. However, for the home-constructor the SPO256 and its allophone system probably represents the most practical approach to speech synthesis.

We will consider allophones and the formation of words in more detail later, but first we will take a look at the SPO256 chip and how it is used.

SPO256

The SPO256 is a very complex device which contains a 2 k × 8-bit ROM, a clock oscillator, control logic, a digital filter (to model the human vocal track), and a pulse width modulator. Although the device is very complex in the way it operates, fortunately most of this complexity is not apparent to the user, and it is not particularly difficult to interface this device to a microcomputer.

Figure 7 shows the pin-out diagram for the SPO256 speech chip. It requires the usual (for logic circuits) single +5 volt supply. Some of the pins are to enable future expan-

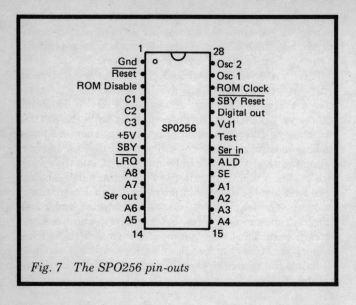

1			28
Gnd			Osc 2
Reset			Osc 1
ROM Disable			ROM Clock
C1			SBY Reset
C2			Digital out
C3	SP0256		Vd1
+5V			Test
SBY			Ser in
LRQ			ALD
A8			SE
A7			A1
Ser out			A2
A6			A3
A5			A4
14			15

Fig. 7   The SPO256 pin-outs

sion with additional ROMs, but these are not really needed, and a perfectly good speech synthesiser can be made using just the basic facilities provided by the SPO256. Therefore, we will not consider these expansion facilities and pins here.

There are eight address inputs (A1 to A8), but A7 and A8 are not normally used, and are simply connected to the negative supply rail. The lower six address inputs are used to select the desired allophone. These could be fed from address lines of the computer, with the appropriate address being POKEd (with any number) to select the required allophone. However, in most cases this would be a rather cumbersome way of doing things, and it is usually better to drive the address lines from the data bus of the computer. In fact, correct timing of the control signals to the SPO256 is essential if it is to operate properly, and a method that seems to invariably give good results is to feed the address lines from the data lines via a latching parallel output port. Parallel output ports were discussed in BP130: *Micro Interfacing Circuits – Book 1*, and will not be considered again here.

20

In operation, the SPO256 is reminiscent of an analogue-to-digital converter. It has an input that is pulsed low in order to activate the device so that it produces the allophone selected by the address fed to its address bus. A status output must then be monitored until it indicates that the allophone has been completed. The next address can then be fed to the address bus, the trigger input is pulsed again, the status output is monitored, and so on, until all the allophones have been completed.

Pin 20 (ALD) is the input that is used to trigger the device, and this requires a brief negative pulse. The status output is pin 9 (LRQ), and this is normally at logic 0, but goes high when the device is producing an allophone. Therefore, after triggering the ALD input the LRQ output goes high, and further allophones must not be loaded until it goes low again. In practice a software loop would normally be used to provide the hold-off until the LRQ output goes low.

There is an alternative way of using the SPO256, although I have never tried out this mode. If pin 19 (SE or Strobe Enable) is taken low, the ALD input is disabled. The device then automatically latches the address on its address bus approximately 1 μs after a logic 1 is detected on any address line. This system could be useful where there is a lack of control lines available, since it can be implemented using just six outputs to drive the address bus and one input to monitor the LRQ output.

The digital output at pin 24 has what is perhaps a rather ambiguous name. This is in fact the audio output, but it is in the form of a pulse-width-modulated digital signal. In other words, the output signal from this is at a constant frequency, and is actually at a high frequency just outside the audio frequency range. The signal is a series of pulses, and by varying the pulse width the average output voltage can be varied. For instance, with a long pulse width so that the pulses virtually merge together the average output voltage would be almost equal to the 5-volt supply potential. On the other hand, with very brief pulses the average output voltage would be practically zero. With no modulation the output has a one-to-one mark-space ratio so that the average output

21

voltage is about half the supply voltage.

In order to recover the audio frequency output signal it is merely necessary to use a low-pass filter to eliminate the high-frequency carrier signal, and leave an output potential equal to the average voltage of the carrier. A filter cut-off frequency of 5 kHz is recommended by the SPO256 manufacturer.

Practical Circuit

Figure 8 shows a practical circuit using the SPO256, but this does not include the interfacing to the microprocessor. All that is needed here is a parallel port capable of providing seven outputs and one input, and a parallel interface device such as a 6821 or 6522 is more than adequate. In fact only one of the ports would be needed, and some computers have a user port which would provide the necessary input/output lines. Of course, TTL devices could be used to provide the interfacing, with (say) seven flip/flops of a 74LS273 being used as data latches to provide the outputs to drive the device, and one section of a 74LS125 quad tristate buffer being used to provide an input so that the LRQ line could be read.

If, for example, the circuit was to be driven from one port of a 6522 VIA or a 6821 PIA, one way of doing things would be to use the six least-significant data lines as outputs to drive the address inputs of the SPO256, with the two remaining data lines being utilised as an output to drive the ALD line, and an input to read the LRQ line. Alternatively, the CA1 and CA2 (or CB1 and CB2 lines, as appropriate) could be used to provide the handshaking with the ALD and LRQ lines. The CA2/CB2 lines could be programmed as a strobe output which would automatically provide a negative pulse each time fresh data was sent to the synthesiser. The CA1/CB1 line could be set as a high/low transition input to monitor the LRQ output. A REPEAT .... UNTIL loop (or similar software loop) would then be used to provide the hold-off until the SPO256 was ready for the next allophone. The allophone addresses could conveniently be held in a DATA statement used in conjunction with (say) a FOR .... NEXT loop. It is a matter of choosing whatever method of inter-

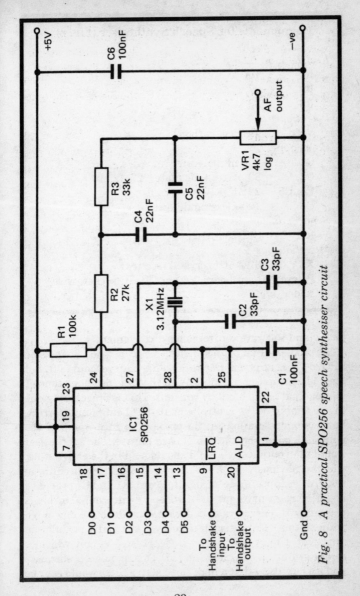

Fig. 8 A practical SPO256 speech synthesiser circuit

23

Components for Speech Synthesiser (Fig. 8)

Resistors, all 0.25 W   5%
R1	100 k
R2	27 k
R3	33 k

Potentiometer
VR1	4k7 log. carbon

Capacitors
C1	100 nF polyester
C2, C3	33 pF ceramic plate 2% (2 off)
C4, C5	22 nF polyester (2 off)
C6	100 nF ceramic

Semiconductor
IC1	SPO256-AL2

Miscellaneous
X1	3.12 MHz crystal (see text)

Printed circuit board, 28-pin DIL IC socket, wire, solder, etc.

facing and software control is most convenient.

A problem that can sometimes occur when using the SPO256 is that of the final allophone not switching off, but instead continuing indefinitely so that a continuous tone or noise signal is produced by the unit. This is presumably due to the timing of the control signals not being quite correct, but a simple solution to the problem is to use one of the pause allophones at the end of each phrase. The synthesiser would then output silence if it should hold in the active state, which is obviously quite acceptable. The discrete circuitry of the synthesiser is quite straightforward. R1 and C1 provide a negative reset pulse for the device at switch-on, and this is primarily to ensure that it does not produce an unwanted audio output. The filtering to recover the audio modulation is provided by a simple two-stage passive circuit which is comprised of R2, C4, R3, and C5. This should be adequate and it is unlikely that a high slope active filter would ever be needed. VR1 is the volume control.

It may be possible to feed the audio signal into an audio input on the computer, and many home-computers have this facility. Alternatively, the audio amplifier circuit which was described earlier (Figure 4) could be used to enable a loud-speaker to be driven.

Clock Oscillator

As mentioned earlier, the SPO256 has a built-in clock oscillator, and this is primarily intended for crystal control. The only discrete components required are the crystal itself (X1), and capacitors C2 and C3. The circuit is intended for use with a 3.12 MHz crystal, but it is not essential to use one having precisely this operating frequency. A frequency of up to about 200 kHz either side of this frequency should give perfectly acceptable results, and the main effect of using a different clock frequency is that it raises or lowers the pitch of the output signal. It also results in the speech being slowed down or speeded up slightly, but this effect tends to be less noticeable. It is possible to use an inductor instead of the crystal, and a value of about 100 μH is suitable. The clock frequency can then be altered to give any desired speech pitch by changing the values of C2 and C3 (which should be kept roughly equal in value).

In some cases the computer may have a clock output at a frequency of about 3.12 MHz, and it should then be possible to use this signal. C2, C3, and X1 would be omitted, and the clock signal would be applied to pin 27 of IC1.

There is a more sophisticated way of using the device, and that is to have a voltage-controlled oscillator to provide the clock signal (with its output driving pin 27). The point of using a VCO is that it would enable the clock frequency to be varied under software control so that changes in the voice pitch could be programmed. This could aid intelligibility slightly, and would certainly give a more realistic and less mechanical-sounding output. Ideally the VCO would be controlled via a digital-to-analogue converter, but more simple arrangments with perhaps just a single digital output to give two voice pitches could be quite effective. However, rapid changes in the voice pitch should be avoided, with a C–R smoothing network being used if necessary. One section of a 74LS629 dual-TTL VCO would be suitable as the basis of the clock oscillator if pitch modulation is to be tried.

Allophones

An important point to keep in mind when selecting allophones is that it is not a matter of just selecting an allophone for each letter of the word or phrase to be produced. Letters have more than one pronounciation, some are not sounded at all, and others operate together to indicate a single sound. It is for this reason that there are 26 letters in the alphabet but 64 allophones in the SPO256.

The list of allophones given below therefore include sample words which help to give a good idea of the actual sound that each one provides. When selecting allophones it is a matter of thinking about the constituent sounds of a word, and then searching through the list to find the best match. The allophones include pauses of five different durations, and this avoids having to use software timing loops or something of this nature to provide pauses between words, etc. A point which is perhaps not obvious is that spaces are not always needed between words due to the way that we tend to join words together in normal speech. Conversely, a short pause placed within a word can sometimes help intelligibility. It is really a matter of thinking about how the word or phrase is spoken and then choosing the appropriate allophones, including pauses, rather than using the way the word or phrase is written down as the basis of the choice. Some allophones are best if preceded by a short pause, and the ones in this category are those that have an abrupt start such as allophones 28, 33, 61, and 63.

With a few allophones it is possible to use two or more in succession to provide a longer sound, but in most cases this is not possible. It is only allophones 7, 12, 15, 23, 24, 26, 29, 30, 40, and 55 that are likely to be usable in this way. In several instances there are allophones which seem to be duplicates or near-duplicates of others. This is where the two sounds

26

are the same or very similar, but one is longer in duration than the other. In these cases it is a good idea to try both versions to determine which one sounds the best in the particular word you are trying to produce.

Address (decimal)	Allophone	Address (decimal)	Allophone
0	10 ms pause	32	OUt
1	30 ms pause	33	Dog
2	50 ms pause	34	pIG
3	100 ms pause	35	Vest
4	200 ms pause	36	GUest
5	tOY	37	SHine
6	flY	38	aZure
7	End	39	bRave
8	Come	40	Find
9	Power	41	sKy
10	dodGe	42	Camera
11	biN	43	Zoo
12	pIn	44	raNG
13	To	45	Light
14	Ran	46	Win
15	sUcceed	47	repaiR
16	Man	48	WHen
17	carT	49	Yet
18	THey	50	CHair
19	sEE	51	tURn
20	bAy	52	cERtain
21	coulD	53	tOW
22	dO	54	THere
23	AUght	55	beSt
24	tOp	56	Now
25	YEt	57	Home
26	bAt	58	stORe
27	Hat	59	bARn
28	Ban	60	cleAR
29	THin	61	Gone
30	lOOk	62	saddLe
31	fOOd	63	draB

When first using the SPO256 it can be a little difficult to obtain good results, but after a little experience with the synthesiser has been gained it becomes much easier to obtain a voice output that is easily understood.

D/A Converters

There are ways of generating audio signals using a computer apart from using a special audio- or speech-synthesiser chip. A common approach is to use a digital-to-analogue converter, such as the circuit using the ZN428 device which was provided in BP130: *Micro Interfacing Circuits – Book 1*. With suitable driving software the output voltage can be varied in any desired manner and any audio waveform can be produced. Of course, the output waveform is stepped (with 256 different output levels being provided in the case of the ZN428), but provided the voltage is stepped up and down at a fast rate the unwanted frequencies produced by this stepping action will be so high that they will be inaudible (although it might be advisable to filter them out anyway). Alternatively, a low-pass filter at the output of the circuit could be used to smooth out the steps to give the required continuous waveform and remove any unwanted audio frequencies.

While this method of producing audio signals is very versatile, and in theory could be used to synthesise any desired audio signal, it does have one major drawback. This is the problem of producing suitable software to give the desired effect. In order to obtain a suitably high operating speed it is necessary to use machine code, and even quite simple waveforms can require a loop to repeatedly output several hundred pieces of data to the D/A converter. However, it does represent an interesting area of experiment for those who have the requisite programming skills.

For this type of sound generation it is not essential to use a high-quality digital-to-analogue converter, and a simple arrangement of the type shown in Figure 9 should give quite good results. This takes the eight latching outputs of a 6522 (or any other 8-bit parallel output) and feeds them into a resistor network which acts as a sort of simple summing cir-

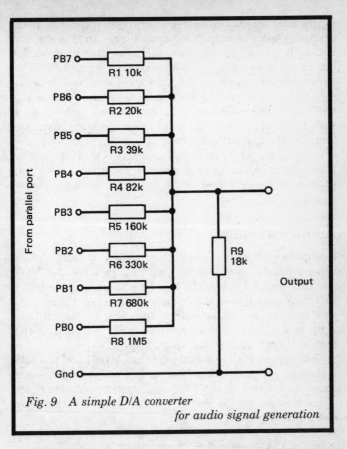

Fig. 9 A simple D/A converter
for audio signal generation

cuit. However, as resistors R1 to R8 are not all the same
value, when set high some outputs produce a greater rise in
output voltage than do others. In fact the resistor values
have been arranged so that there is an approximate doubling
in value from one bit to the next (starting with the most-
significant bit). This gives roughly the correct weighting so
that a simple digital-to-analogue-converter action is obtained, and although the accuracy of this system is at best,
poor, it is perfectly adequate to enable audio waveforms to be

synthesised reasonably well, and is extremely inexpensive if a suitable parallel output port is available. In this application 8-bit resolution is not essential, and quite good results can be achieved using just 6 bits (i.e. omit R8 and R7). The circuit provides an output of up to about 4 volts peak to peak.

A point worth bearing in mind is that devices such as the 6522 have timer/counters which can be used to generate a wide range of output frequencies using the same basic system as that employed in the 8910/12 sound generators. Apart from audio frequency generation, devices of this type can be useful for such things as division of the system clock frequency to provide a lower clock frequency for a peripheral circuit.

Audio Switching

It is quite easy to provide computer control of audio signals using a parallel port to drive electronic switches. A CMOS analogue switch (such as the 4051BE which was discussed in BP130: *Micro Interfacing Circuits – Book 1*) is perfectly suitable for this type of application, but there are special analogue switch devices which are specifically intended for the control of high-quality audio signals.

Two devices in this category are the LM1037 and LM1038 4-channel stereo switches. The basic circuits for these are shown in Figures 10 and 11. Note that in both circuits only one stereo channel is shown, but the circuit for the other channel is identical (the IC pin numbers for the other channel are shown in parenthesis). Both devices require a supply potential in the range 5 to 28 volts, have a channel separation of 95 dB, give 90 dB suppression of unselected channels, a noise output voltage of just 5 μV, and a total harmonic distortion level of 0.04% with a 1-volt RMS input. Both also have four inputs and one output per stereo channel. In other words, they effectively operate as a four-way stereo selector circuit. In fact more channels can be accommodated by using two devices with pin 7 of each device connected together. The left-hand outputs are connected together as are the right-hand outputs, and only one output coupling capacitor is

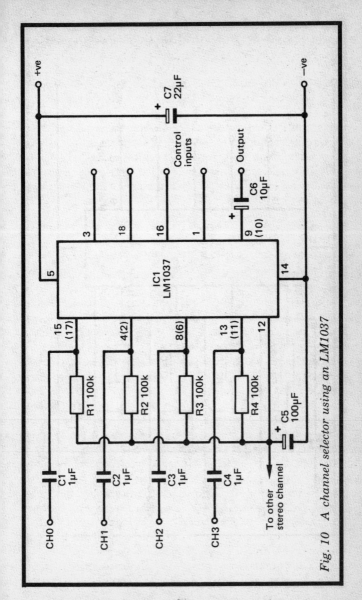

Fig. 10 A channel selector using an LM1037

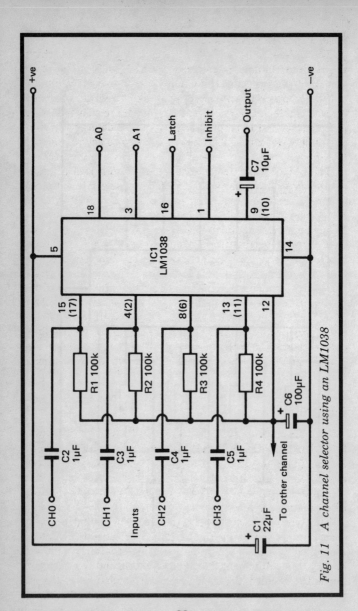

Fig. 11 A channel selector using an LM1038

32

needed for each stereo output.

The difference between the two chips is the way in which the desired channel is selected. The LM1037 is the more simple of the two, and this simply has four control inputs, and the appropriate one of these is taken high to select the desired channel. Channels A, B, C, and D are selected using pins 1, 3, 16, and 18 respectively. With both devices any voltage of between 2 and 50 volts can be used to activate a control input.

The LM1038 has two address inputs, and it is the binary address placed on these that is used to select the desired channel. There are two other control inputs, and the "Inhibit" input cuts off all the audio inputs when it is taken high. In most practical applications this would not be required and would simply be tied to the negative supply rail. The final control input is used to latch addresses, and it controls a form of transparent latch at the address inputs. A negative-to-positive transition is used to latch addresses, and in theory it should be possible to control the device directly from the data bus of the microprocessor, with the latching pulse provided by an address-decoder circuit. If the circuit is driven from a parallel port having latching outputs the "Latch" input is not needed and is tied to the positive supply rail.

Digital Filter

Where a computer-controlled filter is required, one solution to the problem would be to use an ordinary voltage-controlled filter driven via a digital-to-analogue converter. These days there is an alternative method that can be used, and this is to use a so-called digital filter, or switched-capacitor filter as they are also known.

This type of filter is based on an electronic switch and two capacitors as shown in Figure 12. The electronic switch is controlled by a clock oscillator operating at a fairly high frequency (typically about 20 kHz to 1 MHz), and the basic action of the circuit is for C1 to be repeatedly charged to the input potential, and then connected across C2 (and the output

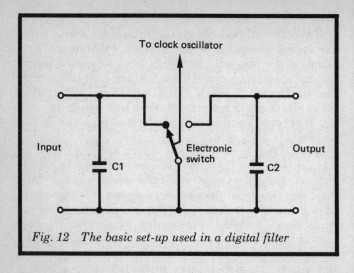

Fig. 12   *The basic set-up used in a digital filter*

of the filter). If the charge on C1 is greater than that on C2, C1 discharges into C2 until the two have an equal charge potential. If C2 has the greater charge, it discharges into C1 until they have the same charge potential.

The effect of this is to keep C2 at a similar charge to the potential present at the input. However, C1 is made far lower in value than C2, and it is only possible for the output to be maintained at virtually the same voltage as the input if the clock frequency is much higher than the input frequency. C1 can then provide a large enough charge transfer to do this. The circuit is actually not that different to an ordinary R–C low-pass filter, and the switch plus C1 are used to replace the resistor of a conventional R–C filter. The higher the clock frequency, the greater the charge transfer that can be achieved, the lower the effective resistance of the switch and C1, and the higher the cutoff frequency of the filter.

The point of this type of filter is that its cutoff frequency can be controlled by a clock signal, which can be generated by a digital circuit (such as a timer/counter of a 6522 VIA). Computer control of the cutoff frequency is therefore quite straightforward.

MF10CN Filter

The MF10CN is a very useful digital filter which is reasonably inexpensive (for a device of this type anyway). It actually contains two second-order (12 dB per octave) switched-capacitor filters, and these are both state-variable types. In other words, apart from the basic low-pass filters there is some additional circuitry that enables a variety of filter types to be produced. In fact low-pass, high-pass, band-pass, notch, and all-pass modes are obtainable. The filter frequency can be either $\frac{1}{100}$th or $\frac{1}{50}$th of the clock frequency with a typical error of under 1%.

Figure 13 shows a filter circuit based on the MF10CN. This only uses one section of the device (the pin numbers in parenthesis are for the other section). The circuit requires dual 5-volt supplies, but the clock signal only needs to be an ordinary TTL or CMOS signal and does not need to go negative of the 0-volt (GND) supply rail. As shown the circuit has a cutoff frequency which is $\frac{1}{100}$th of the clock frequency, but this can be changed to $\frac{1}{50}$th by connecting pin 12 to the +5-volt supply rail.

The MF10CN has an operational-amplifier input stage, and R2 plus R4 are used to bias this and set its voltage gain at unity. R3 provides feedback from the band-pass output of the filter. With the output taken from pin 1, as in this circuit, a low-pass filter action is obtained. However, by taking the output from pin 3 or pin 2 notch or band-pass filtering can be obtained. A different configuration is needed for high-pass and all-pass filtering. The value of R3 controls the Q of the filter, and with the specified value the Q is 1. A higher value gives increased Q, and a lower value produces reduced Q.

R1 and C2 form a simple low-pass filter at the input of the circuit. These attenuate any high-frequency signals which might otherwise break through into the filter and react with the clock signal to produce heterodynes. R5 and C3 form a simple low-pass filter at the output of the unit, and this helps to reduce breakthrough of the clock signal to the output. The clock signal level at the output of the MF10CN is only about

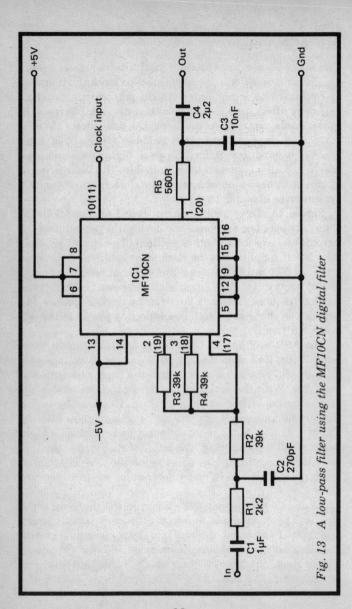

Fig. 13 A low-pass filter using the MF10CN digital filter

36

10 mV, and a simple passive filter of this type is usually sufficient to reduce it to a level that will not cause any problems with the equipment fed from the output of the circuit.

A point that should be borne in mind is that the clock frequency should not be less that about 20 kHz or any slight breakthrough to the output will be audible. This could be overcome by using a high-performance low-pass filter to attenuate the clock breakthrough to an inaudible level, but this would obviously restrict the upper audio response of the circuit which would be unacceptable in some applications. On the other hand, in some applications such as certain types of test gear, a 10 mV breakthrough of the clock signal at the output would be totally unimportant. It would then be possible to have the clock frequency as low as desired, and the output low-pass filter would be unnecessary.

VCA

To the best of my knowledge there is no volume control equivalent to a digital filter, and circuits that provide digital control of gain actually consist of a digital-to-analogue converter driving a voltage-controlled amplifier of some kind. At the time of writing a few digital volume control devices are produced, but they are few in number, difficult to obtain, and quite expensive. Of course, virtually any conventional VCA circuit could be driven by a digital-to-analogue converter to provide a digital volume control. However, the expense of a high-quality digital-to-analogue converter is not normally justified, and a more simple arrangement such as the one employed in the circuit of Figure 14 is often perfectly adequate.

This is basically just a standard VCA built around one section of an LM13600N (or LM13700N) dual-transconductance operational amplifier. The numbers in parenthesis give the pin numbers for the second section of the device.

R9, R10, and C2 effectively provide a centre tap on the supply lines, while R11 to R13 are used to bias IC1. R16 is the load resistor for the emitter-follower output stage of IC1.

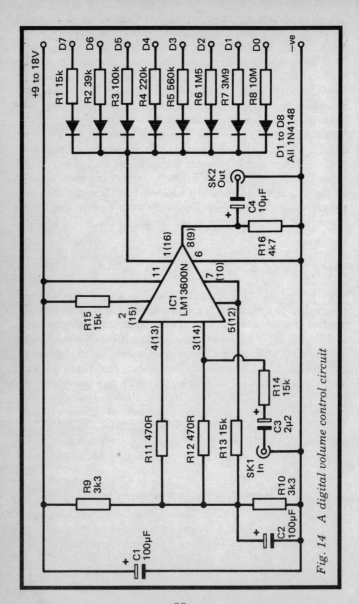

Fig. 14 A digital volume control circuit

Components for Digital Volume Control (Fig. 14)

Resistors, all 0.25 W   5%

R1	15 k
R2	39 k
R3	100 k
R4	220 k
R5	560 k
R6	1M5
R7	3M9
R8	10 M
R9, R10	3k3 (2 off)
R11, R12	470 R (2 off)
R13–R15	15 k (3 off)
R16	4k7

Capacitors

C1	100 µF 25 V electrolytic
C2	100 µF 10 V electrolytic
C3	2.2 µF 50 V electrolytic
C4	10 µF 25 V electrolytic

Semiconductors

IC1	LM13600N (or LM13700N)
D1–D8	1N4148 (8 off)

Miscellaneous

Printed circuit board, input and output sockets, wire, solder, etc.

R14 is used to reduce the maximum voltage gain of the circuit to about unity, and it boosts the input impedance of the unit from about 470 R to a more usable figure of around 5 k. R15 is the bias resistor for the linearising diodes, and this helps to give improved noise and distortion performance.

The voltage gain of the circuit is roughly proportional to the bias current fed into pin 1 (16), and strictly speaking, the circuit is a current-controlled amplifier rather than a voltage-controlled type. The outputs of an 8-bit parallel (latching) port are coupled to the control input of IC1 by way of eight resistors, one for each output. The resistors which are suitably weighted so that an appropriate degree of control is provided by each bit. A diode is needed in series with each resistor so that it can add to the control current when the output driving it is set high, but it cannot tap off any of the control current when the output driving it is set low.

The control range of the circuit is quite wide, with about 70 dB or more of attenuation being provided when only input D0 is set high. There is around 90 dB of attenuation when all the control inputs are low and IC1 is cut off. With some 256 different gain settings the voltage gain can be varied smoothly with the stepping up and down in gain not being apparent to the listener, due to the smallness of the steps. In fact, the gain can be varied by increments of well under 1 dB.

For stereo operation the second section of IC1 could, of course, be used in the same basic circuit. The gain of the two channels could be controlled separately with an 8-bit output port being used for each stereo channel. Alternatively, the control pins of the two sections of IC1 could be wired together and driven from a common resistor/diode network. In this case though, the control current would be split between the two sections of IC1, and to compensate for this the values of R1 to R8 would have to be approximately halved. Incidentally, the control inputs should be fed from an output that provides ordinary 5-volt logic signals, and the circuit will operate properly using any supply voltage in the range 9 to 18 volts. Signals of up to about 2 volts RMS can be handled before clipping and serious distortion occur.

CHAPTER 2

Light and Temperature

In this chapter we will consider interfacing to opto-electric devices, including such topics as driving seven-segment LED displays, counting circuits using opto-electric sensors, and simple light-level detector circuits. Devices for temperature sensing and measurement will also be discussed.

Display Driving

Home-computers normally use a television or monitor to display information, but there are applications where the use of a television or monitor is not desirable. For example, in an application where the computer is left operating continuously for long periods of time, and is often left unattended, some simple form of status display would probably be perfectly adequate. This would avoid unnecessary wear on the television or monitor, which should not be left running and unattended anyway as it could represent a fire hazard. In an application such as a computerised darkroom the amount of light generated by a television or monitor might be unacceptable.

A status display can take a variety of forms, and could simply consist of something like a flashing LED driven from an output port to indicate that the program is running properly and that the computer has not crashed. A slightly more sophisticated display could use a series of LEDs, or a proper bargraph display, to indicate the progress of the program through a number of stages. Provided an 8-LED display was adequate the LEDs could be driven from an 8-bit latching output port. For a greater number of LEDs one solution would be to use two 8-bit output ports, but it would probably be better to use a four to 16-line decoder, as shown in Figure 15. This requires just four latching outputs to drive 16 LEDs.

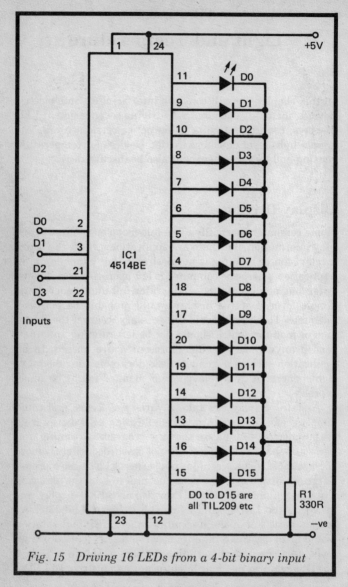

Fig. 15 Driving 16 LEDs from a 4-bit binary input

The device used in this circuit is a CMOS 4514BE. This has four inputs, and the binary number fed to these selects the output which goes high. Only one output will go high at any one time, and therefore only one of the LEDs (D0 to D15) will be activated at any one time. Assuming that the four inputs are driven from the lower four bits of the output port and the four most-significant bits are unused, the number POKEd to the port will cause the LED having the corresponding number to be switched on. As the LEDs are only switched on one at a time a single current-limiting resistor (R1) for all sixteen LEDs is acceptable. The specified value for R1 gives a LED current of about 7 to 8 milliamps.

Pin 23 of IC1 is the inhibit input, which can be set high to turn off all sixteen outputs. Pin 1 is the strobe input, and is not needed in an application where the circuit is driven from a latching port. This is simply taken to the positive supply rail. This could be fed with a positive pulse from an address decoder to latch the data fed to the four data inputs, so that the latter could be fed directly from the data bus. However, in practice CMOS devices are not always compatible with microprocessor circuits, and this might not give reliable results in all cases.

Seven-segment

An alternative form of LED display, and one which is perhaps more easily read, is the seven-segment type. These have the segments arranged in the familiar figure-of-eight pattern, as shown in Figure 16. The segments have standard identification letters from a to g, as shown in the diagram. By activating the appropriate segments a reasonably clear representation of any single digit number can be produced (segments a, b, and c to produce a figure 7 for example).

If an 8-bit latching output port is available this could be used to drive a seven-segment LED display, with the software being used to provide the decoding and switch on the appropriate segments. This is a rather cumbersome way of doing things, especially if buffering is needed to give suffi-

43

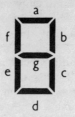

Fig. 16   The arrangement used in a
seven-segment LED display

cient current drive for the display. A more efficient way of tackling things is to use a seven-segment display driver/ decoder as shown in Figure 17.

This uses the CMOS 4511BE decoder/driver and a DL704 seven-segment LED display. The circuit should work perfectly well using most other LED displays, but note that only common cathode types can be directly driven by the 4511BE. The LED current is again around 7 to 8 milliamps, but as several segments will be driven at once the total LED current can exceed 60 milliamps, and a separate current-limiting resistor is needed for each segment. Provided the four inputs are fed from the four least-significant bits of the output port and the upper four bits are left unused, the number POKEd to the port will appear on the display. However, only numbers from 0 to 9 can be accommodated. It would be possible to drive a second 4511BE display from the upper four bits of the port so that two-digit numbers could be produced, but the software to handle this could be more difficult than one might expect.

Pin 3 of IC1 is the LT (lamp test) input, and if this is taken to the negative supply rail all seven segments of the display are switched on. A BL (blank lamp) input is available at pin 4, and taking this pin low switches off all the display segments. Neither facility is likely to be needed in this

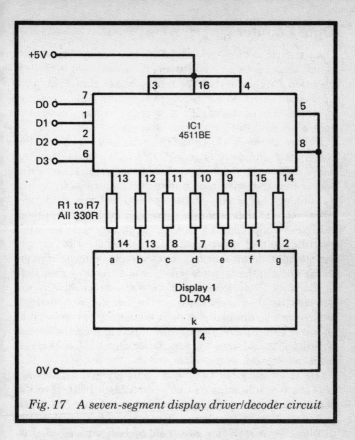

Fig. 17 A seven-segment display driver/decoder circuit

context, and consequently both of these pins are just wired to
the positive supply rail. Pin 5 is the strobe input, and a latching action is provided if this is normally high and a negative
latching pulse is used. If the inputs are fed from a latching
output port pin 5 is simply tied to the negative supply rail. In
some cases it might be possible to drive the inputs directly
from the data bus with a latching pulse being provided by an
address decoder.

45

Opto Counter

Opto-electric devices are useful as the basis of automatic counting and sensing circuits, and are much used in this application. Circuits of this type tend to be associated only with applications such as batch counters, but they also find uses in things such as slot-car lap counters and timers, computer-controlled model railways, and robotics.

Figure 18 shows a circuit of this type which uses an infra-red emitter and detector pair (D1 and D2 respectively). An advantage of the infra-red devices in an application of this sort is that they give good immunity to spurious triggering by ambient light. This is due to the low level of ambient infra-red light that is normally present, even when artificial (tungsten lamp) lighting is used. D2 incorporates an infra-red filter so that it is almost totally insensitive to ordinary visible light, despite the fact that the semiconductor element at the heart of the device is sensitive to a broad range of light frequencies. The circuit is of the type where objects are detected as they pass between the emitter and detector devices, which are placed a short distance apart. As well as counting applications, two circuits of this type can be used in a set-up that measures the time taken for an object to travel from one detector to the other.

D1 is an infra-red LED, and is simply given a forward bias of a few milliamps, just like an ordinary LED. The LED current is about 7 milliamps with R1 at the specified value, and this gives a maximum operating range of about 30 millimetres or so. The range could be boosted somewhat by using a higher LED current of up to 50 milliamps, but this type of circuit is not usable where large objects must be detected, and the two cells must consequently be positioned some distance apart.

The detector diode is reverse biased by R2, and a small leakage current flows through R2 and D2. The precise current flow depends on the intensity of the infra-red light received by D2, and is roughly proportional to this infra-red level. As D2 normally receives a strong dose of infra-red radiation from D1 the stand-by current flow through these

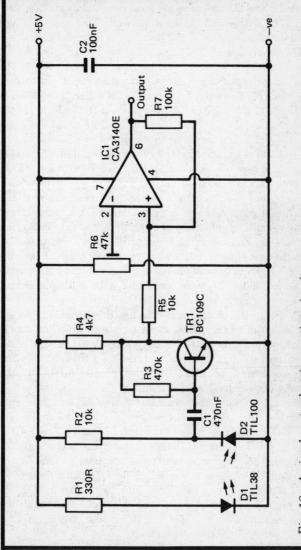

Fig. 18 A simple opto-electric counting circuit

components is relatively high. When an object passes between D1 and D2 the infra-red level received by D2 falls dramatically, as does the leakage current. This gives a small positive voltage pulse at the junction of R2 and D2.

The amplitude of this pulse is far too low to drive a logic input, and must be amplified considerably. C1 couples the pulse to the input of a high-gain common emitter-amplifier based on Tr1. The amplified signal is then directly coupled to the input of a Schmitt trigger (based on IC1) which shapes the signal to give a "clean" output pulse. R5 couples the collector of Tr1 to the non-inverting input of operational amplifier IC1. R6 is used to bias the inverting input of IC1, and is adjusted to give a bias potential which is slightly lower than the potential at the non-inverting input of IC1. This results in the output of IC1 going high under quiescent conditions.

When a positive pulse is produced by D2 a much larger negative pulse is generated at the collector of Tr1. This briefly takes the non-inverting input of IC1 to a lower potential than the inverting input, giving a negative pulse at the output of IC1. R7 is used to provide a certain amount of hysteresis which helps to avoid problems with multiple output pulses being generated each time the circuit is activated.

To set up the circuit ready for use R6 should first be set for maximum voltage at its wiper terminal. It is then slowly backed off until the output of IC1 switches to the high state. The circuit should then give good results, although it is probably worthwhile backing off R6 marginally further in the interest of good long-term reliability.

The pulse length generated by the unit is largely dependent on the time taken for each object to pass between the sensors. If the objects do not pass through in about 0.1 seconds or less the low-frequency response of the circuit may be inadequate, and the unit may not function properly. This can be overcome by using a higher value for C1. The circuit obviously has a finite response time, and a very fast-moving object might be too fast for the unit to detect it, although the response time is quite short and this would only occur with an exceptionally fast-moving object.

Obviously any normal 5-volt digital input could be used to

monitor the output of the circuit, but the software will probably be easier to design if an edge-sensitive input is used. It is then just a matter of designing the software to count the number of positive or negative transitions produced by the circuit. A handshake input of an interface device such as the 6522 or 6821 is ideal for this type of application.

A point worth bearing in mind is that IC1 is one of the few operational amplifiers that will operate from a supply voltage as low as 5 volts, and it should not be substituted with an ordinary operational amplifier (such as a 741C), which will not. One final point is that it is essential to aim the output of D1 at the most sensitive surface of D2 if reasonably good results are to be attained. The sensitive surface of D2 is a large one, opposite the side marked with the type number, etc.

Passive Detector

For some applications a passive detector circuit will suffice. This type of circuit does not transmit any form of light beam, but relies on a change in the received light level being produced as the object to be detected passes. Passive detectors can actually be quite effective, and it is not usually too difficult to arrange things so that the background contrasts well with the objects to be detected, and a large change in light level is produced. Passive detectors can operate over distances of up to about 1 metre, but obviously the maximum range obtained is very much dependent on the conditions under which the equipment has to operate.

Figure 19 shows the circuit diagram of a simple but efficient passive detector circuit. This is based on the previous circuit, and only really differs from this in that the emitter section has been omitted, and the detector diode has been replaced by a photo-Darlington transistor. The change in the detector device is required since we are interested in the visible part of the light spectrum in this instance, and good sensitivity is needed. A photo-Darlington is the obvious choice, and any of the common types such as a 2N5777 or MEL12 should give good results in this circuit. It is the

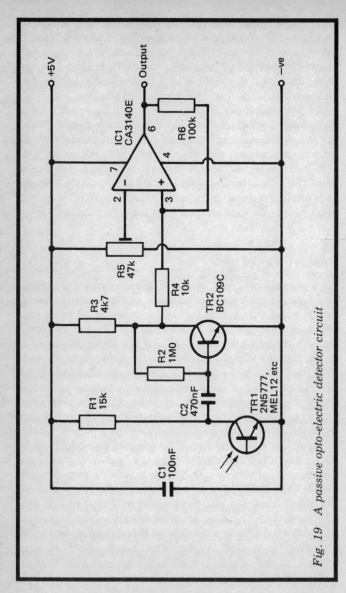

Fig. 19 A passive opto-electric detector circuit

collector-to-emitter leakage current of Tr1 (which is light dependent) that is utilised in this circuit. There is no connection to the base terminal of Tr1.

In practice, Tr1 will probably need to be placed with its sensitive surface looking down a thin tube painted matt-black on the inside. The idea of this is to give the detector good directional properties so that it only detects the correct objects, and is unaffected by anything else moving in its vicinity. An alternative to using a tube is to use a convex lens (although the sensor would still need to be reasonably well shielded from ambient light). The advantage of a lens is that, provided it is correctly positioned and set up, it will concentrate light received over a fairly large area on to the photocell, giving excellent sensitivity. The drawbacks are that a suitable lens could prove to be difficult to obtain, and it would be relatively expensive, and difficult to set up.

An important point to note is that the circuit cannot work properly in total darkness, and that even in the presence of low light levels signals generated by Tr1 are unlikely to be large enough to operate the unit properly. The specified value for R1 should give good results, but it would probably be possible to obtain improved range and reliability if the value of this component was selected to suit the conditions under which the circuit will operate. This is just a matter of experimenting with a few values to determine which one gives optimum results. The circuit will also work quite well using a cadmium sulphide photo-resistor in place of TR1, but the response time of this type of cell is significantly slower than a photo-Darlington one.

Echo Sensor

This is another type of active sensor, and it uses an infra-red emitter and detector mounted more or less side by side. Normally there is little pick-up of the transmitted signal by the detector since the output of the emitter is aimed away from the detector cell. However, if an object passes in front of the cells it will reflect some of the infra-red radiation back towards the receiver, and it is this echo that is used to activate the receiver and provide the output pulse.

The basic arrangement used in the unit is outlined in the block diagram of Figure 20. With this type of detector a DC circuit is impractical since the amount of infra-red reflected back to the receiver is likely to be extremely small, and totally inadequate to activate a DC circuit reliably. The transmitted signal is therefore in the form of infra-red pulses, at a frequency of around 10 kHz in this case. The transmitter is really just an oscillator which pulses an infra-red LED at a current in the region of 70 milliamps.

The receiver uses an infra-red detector diode feeding into a very high gain AF amplifier. Although the reflected infra-red may only give a signal of under 1 millivolt peak to peak from the detector diode, after amplification the signal level should be a more usable 1 volt peak to peak or thereabouts. This is smoothed and rectified to produce a positive DC bias which is fed into a Schmitt trigger circuit, and this stage converts the rise in output voltage from the smoothing circuit into a proper pulse signal which can be used to drive a logic circuit.

The circuit diagram of the transmitter is shown in Figure 21. This is just a standard 555 astable circuit having the values of the timing component (R1, R2, and C2) chosen to give a suitable operating frequency. R1 is a current-limiting resistor, and even when operating from a supply voltage as low as 5 volts the output stage of the 555 is able to provide an adequate output current for this application. The output waveform of IC1 is not a one-to-one squarewave, and the mark period is a little over three times longer than the space time. Emitter diode D1 is connected between the output of IC1 and the positive supply rail, so that it is only pulsed on for about 20 to 25% of the time. This does not significantly degrade the performance of the circuit, and helps to keep the average current consumption of the circuit down to a reasonable level (about 25 milliamps in fact).

Figure 22 shows the circuit diagram of the receiver. The detector diode is a TIL100, as used in the circuit of Figure 18 which was described earlier. It is essential for R2 and D1 to

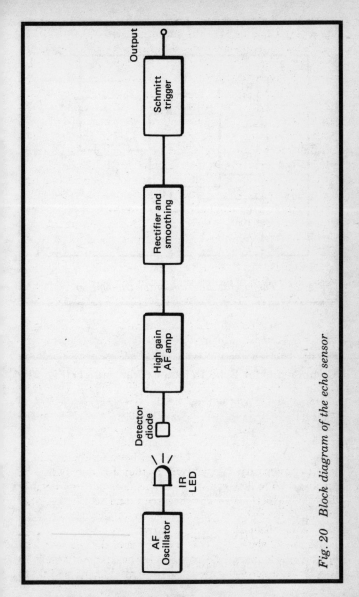

Fig. 20 Block diagram of the echo sensor

53

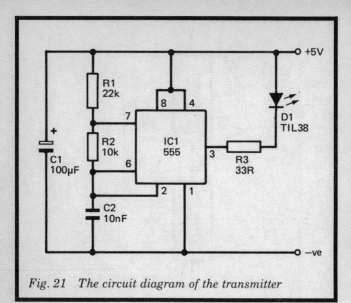

Fig. 21   The circuit diagram of the transmitter

Components for Echo Detector (Transmitter) (Fig. 21)

Resistors, all 0.25 W   5%

    R1   22 k

    R2   10 k

    R3   33 R

Capacitors

    C1   100 μF   10 V electrolytic

    C2   10 nF polyester

Semiconductors

    IC1   555

    D1   TIL38 infra-red LED

Miscellaneous

    Printed circuit board, wire, solder, etc.

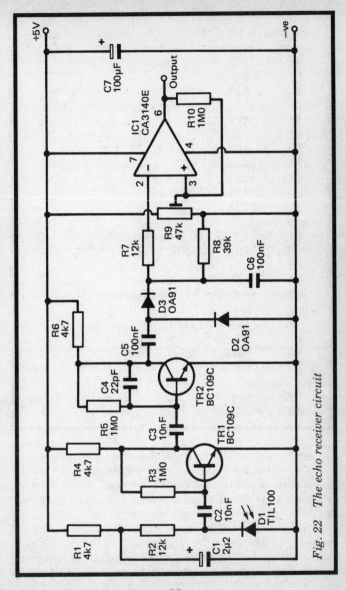

Fig. 22 The echo receiver circuit

55

Components for Echo Detector (Receiver) (Fig. 22)

Resistors, all 0.25 W   5% except R9

R1	4k7
R2	12 k
R3	1 M
R4	4k7
R5	1 M
R6	4k7
R7	12 k
R8	39 k
R9	47 k 0.1 W preset
R10	1 M

Capacitors

C1	2.2 μF 50 V electrolytic
C2, C3	10 nF polyester (2 off)
C4	22 pF ceramic
C5, C6	100 nF polyester (2 off)
C7	100 μF 10 V electrolytic

Semiconductors

Tr1, Tr2	BC109C (2 off)
IC1	CA3140E
D1	TIL100 infra-red detector
D2, D3	OA91 (2 off)

Miscellaneous

Printed circuit board, 8-pin DIL IC socket, wire, solder, etc.

be fed from a well-smoothed and decoupled supply as any noise on the supply to this circuit will be coupled into the input of the amplifier, and could block operation of the unit. R1 and C1 are therefore used to filter the supply to R2 and D1.

The amplifier is a simple two-stage, capacitively-coupled, common emitter type. Coupling capacitors C2 and C3 have purposely been given rather low values so that they provide a very inefficient signal path at low frequencies. The purpose of this is to provide high attenuation at 50 Hz so that any pick-up from mains lighting is reduced to an insignificant level. The signal from the transmitter is at a much higher frequency, where C2 and C3 do provide an efficient coupling. C4 rolls off the radio frequency response of the amplifier, and this helps to avoid problems with high-frequency instability and radio-frequency breakthrough.

C5 couples the output of the amplifier to a conventional rectifier and smoothing circuit which uses D2, D3, C6, and R8. The circuit has quite a fast response time and takes only about a millisecond to respond to a change in the input signal level. The Schmitt trigger is based on IC1 and uses the same configuration as the one used in the passive detector circuit described previously. In order to obtain good sensitivity R10 has been given a higher value in this case so that reduced hysteresis is provided. If necessary though, R10 could be reduced in value to give a more reliable and glitch free output. However, in most applications the specified value should be perfectly satisfactory.

The emitter and detector diodes should be mounted close together and aimed in the same direction. A small amount of breakthrough from the transmitter to the receiver due to stray capacitance in inevitable, but the breakthrough should not be large enough to warrant screening of the receiver. It is essential to shield the detector diode from direct pick-up of the output from the emitter diode, but anything opaque placed between the two diodes will achieve this.

When adjusting R9, start with this set for miminum wiper voltage (which should cause the output to go low). Then slowly adjust it for a higher wiper voltage until the output switches to the high state. Placing your hand just in front of the emitter/detector diodes should result in the output of the unit switching to a low state, and remaining there until your hand is removed.

The range obtained using this system depends to a large extent on the size and other characteristics of the object which must be detected. A large, flat and highly reflective object is likely to give a range of around 150 to 300 millimetres. On the other hand, a small object might give a maximum detection range of only about 25 millimetres, and a very small object might not be detected at all by this system.

Broken Beam Detector

The echo detector circuit can be utilised as a broken beam detector without making any modifications to the circuit. It is simply a matter of having the emitter and detector diodes some distance apart and aimed at one another. A maximum range of about 1 metre or so should be possible with this arrangement. When adjusting R9 it should initially be set for a maximum wiper potential, and then backed off slowly until the output of the circuit switches to the low state. Interrupting the beam should then result in the output switching to the high state.

Light Level Detector

If a light level detector circuit is required it might be possible to use an analogue (potentiometer-type joystick or games paddle) input of the computer in connection with a cadmium sulphide photocell. Of course, not all computers have some form of analogue input, and where a suitable built-in interface is not fitted some form of external circuit will be needed. However, analogue-to-digital converters were covered in BP130: *Micro Interfacing Circuits – Book 1*, and will not be considered again here. The photocell circuit is much the same whether the analogue port it feeds into is an internal part of the computer or a user add-on.

There are two basic types of analogue input: the true analogue-to-digital converter and the resistance-to-digital converter. With the former the input responds to the voltage fed to it, and three examples of computers with this type of input are the BBC model B and the Dragon 32/64 machines. An analogue port added by the user is almost certain to be of this type as well. The second type is usually based on a simple C–R timing circuit, and it is the resistance from the input to (usually) the positive supply rail to which the circuit responds. The games paddle inputs of the Atari, Commodore 64 and VIC-20 machines are examples of this type of converter.

The second type is the easier to use in that it is simply a matter of connecting a cadmium sulphide photoresistor in place of the variable resistor of a games paddle. In order to obtain usable results the photocell must provide a similar resistance range to that provided by the games paddle, which is normally 0 to 470 k. In practice an inexpensive RPY58A cell seems to give good results. For operation at low light levels a more sensitive cell such as an ORP12 might be preferable, and for operation in high light levels a lower sensitivity type such as an ORP60 or ORP61 might be better. A point which should be kept in mind is that the value returned from the port decreases as the light level received by the cell is increased. This is simply because the resistance of the cell decreases with increasing light level.

Interfacing a photocell to an analogue-to-digital converter is almost as easy, and only a load resistor is needed in addition to the photocell. Figure 23 shows the correct method of

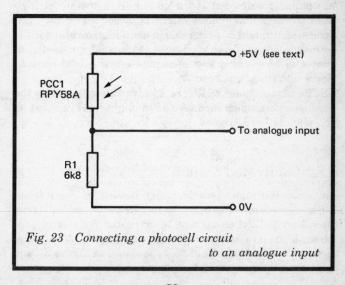

Fig. 23   Connecting a photocell circuit
to an analogue input

connection. It has been assumed here that the digital-to-ana-logue converter has an input voltage range of 0 to 5 volts, as in the case of the Dragon computers for example. This is not always the case though, and the converter in the BBC model B computer, for instance, requires a 0 to 1.8-volt input range. The analogue port of the BBC model B machine includes a 1.8-volt reference output, and the upper end of PCC1 would be connected to this instead of the 5-volt supply rail. The point of doing this is to ensure that the input voltage to the converter cannot go outside its intended operating range.

If the photocell is to be connected to the computer via a long connecting cable it will probably be necessary to include a capacitor of around 1 μF in value in parallel with R1 to prevent noise from spoiling results. This inevitably slows down the response time of the circuit quite significantly though. Note that with a resistance-to-digital converter a fil-ter capacitor must not be wired across the photocell, and that the use of a long connecting cable to the photocell will prob-ably be impractical.

The specified value for load resistor R1 should give acceptable results, but if the circuit is to operate at high light levels a lower value might be needed. For low light operation it might be preferable to use a higher value for R1, although this would be ineffective if the analogue-to-digital converter has a fairly low input impedance. A buffer ampli-fier would then be needed.

The arrangement of Figure 23 gives a reading from the analogue port which increases as the light level received by the photocell is increased.

Light-activated Switch

An analogue input is only really needed in applications where light level must be measured. In many cases it is only necessary for the equipment to act if the light level goes above of falls below a certain threshold value. All this re-quires is a simple circuit of the type shown in Figure 24, and a single-bit digital input for it to drive.

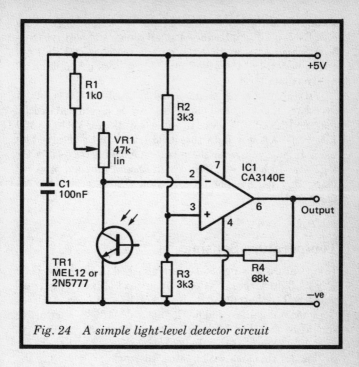

Fig. 24   A simple light-level detector circuit

IC1 has its non-inverting input biased to half the supply potential by R2 and R3. The inverting input of IC1 is biased by the potential divider formed by R1 plus VR1, and the collector-to-emitter resistance of photo-Darlington device Tr1. VR1 is adjusted so that half the supply voltage is fed to IC1's inverting input when Tr1 is subjected to the desired switch-over light level.

If Tr1 is subjected to a higher light level its collector-to-emitter resistance falls, and consequently, so does the voltage fed to the inverting input of IC1. With the inverting input at a lower voltage than the non-inverting input, the output of IC1 goes high. If Tr1 is subjected to a lesser light intensity than the threshold level its increased collector-to-emitter resistance results in a higher voltage being fed to the inverting input of IC1. With its inverting input at a higher voltage than the non-inverting input the output of IC1 goes low. R4 is used to introduce a small amount of positive feedback which ensures that the output switches cleanly from one logic level to the other, and that it does not assume an intermediate level.

VR1 gives a wide range of light threshold levels, but if necessary higher threshold levels can be accommodated by making R1 and VR1 lower in value (say 4k7 for VR1 and 100 R for R1). A lower light threshold level can be obtained by using higher values for these two components (say 470 k for VR1 and 10 k for R1). The circuit should function properly using any normal photo-Darlington transistor in the Tr1 position.

Temperature Sensing

Temperature sensing can be accomplished in much the same way as light level detection, but instead of a cadmium sulphide cell a thermistor is used. For use with an Atari or Commodore games paddle input a VA1067S thermistor should be suitable. Most other thermistors are unlikely to give good results as they have resistance ranges that are far too low for this application. Most thermistors, including the VA1067S, have a negative temperature coefficient. What this means in practice is that increasing temperature returns reducing values from the paddle port. This is not really of great importance in that this simple arrangement is not really suitable for accurate temperature measurement, and is better suited to an application where a threshold temperature must be detected and acted upon. With the thermistor at the required threshold temperature the paddle port can be read to find the corresponding paddle port reading. Even if the system must respond to a number of temperature levels, the same arrangement and setting-up procedure can be used to determine the threshold values.

For a computer that has a normal analogue-to-digital converter which responds to the input potential, the arrangement of Figure 23 (which was described earlier) can be used.

Obviously PCC1 should be replaced with a thermistor. A VA1066S should give good results. Again, this system is far from ideal for temperature measurement applications, even though in this case increasing temperature does return increasing readings from the port. The problem is a lack of linearity over a wide temperature range.

Semiconductor Sensor

There are many semiconductor devices which can be used as acurate temperature sensors, and even the humble silicon diode can give quite good results in this role. There are some useful IC temperature sensors available which give excellent linearity over a wide temperature range, and these are perhaps the type of sensor that is best suited to a computer temperature interface application. Probably the best known device of this type, and one of the most accurate available, is the LM335Z. This is a three-terminal device which is used in the basic arrangement shown in Figure 25.

In effect the LM335Z is a precision (shunt type) voltage regulator, but the voltage produced is temperature dependent. When used with a computer the sensor will presumably be powered from a well stabilised 5-volt supply, but the supply does not really need to be well stabilised. The output voltage of the circuit is equal to 10 millivolts per degree Kelvin, or, to put it another way, 2.73 volts plus 10 millivolts per degree Centigrade. VR1 is adjusted to give an output potential of 2.98 volts with the LM335Z at 25 degrees Centigrade. A wide temperature range of −150 degrees to +150 degrees Centigrade is covered by the device, with excellent linearity. This makes it ideal for applications where accurate temperature measurement is required.

One way of using the LM335Z would be to couple the output of the circuit to the input of an 8-bit digital-to-analogue converter having its input sensitivity set at 5.1 volts. Multiplying the reading returned from the port by two, and then deducting 273 from this value, would give the temperature of the sensor in degrees Centigrade. Although this would cover

63

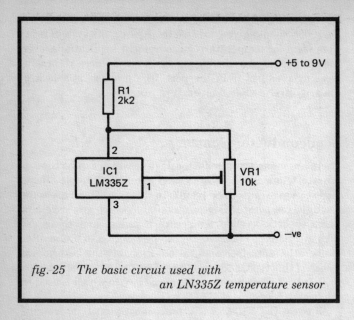

fig. 25   The basic circuit used with
an LN335Z temperature sensor

the full 300-degree range available using the LM335Z, it
would give a resolution of only 2 degrees Centigrade, which
would be inadequate for most purposes. Of course, using
(say) a 12-bit converter would give greatly enhanced resolution and accuracy.

An alternative way of tackling the problem is to use a
level-shifting circuit to effectively bring the output voltage
swing of the temperature sensor circuit into a more suitable
range for the analogue-to-digital converter, so that good
results can be obtained using an ordinary 8-bit type. A level-
shifting circuit which is suitable for this application is shown
in Figure 26.

The output voltage of the temperature sensor is fed to two
unity-voltage gain-inverting amplifiers which are wired in
series. Overall this gives unity-voltage gain and no inver-
sion. However, the voltage at the output of the circuit is not
identical to the input voltage from the sensor circuit, due to
the positive bias voltage that is fed to the non-inverting

64

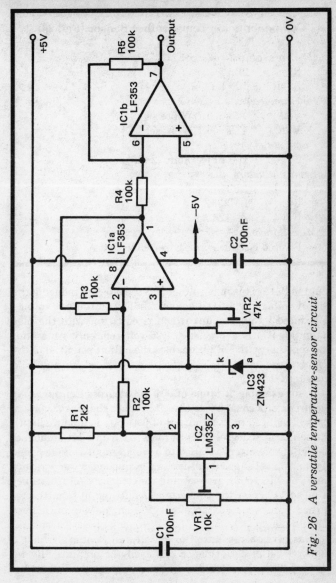

Fig. 26 A versatile temperature-sensor circuit

Components for Temperature Sensor (Fig. 26)

Resistors, all 0.25 W   5%
   R1   2k2
   R2–R5   100 k (4 off)
Potentiometers
   VR1   10 k   0.1 W preset
   VR2   47 k   0.1 W preset
Capacitors
   C1, C2   100 nF ceramic (2 off)
Semiconductors
   IC1   LF353
   IC2   LM335Z
   IC3   ZN423
Miscellaneous
   Printed circuit board, wire, solder, etc.

input of IC1a. This bias voltage has the effect of reducing the output voltage by a fixed amount. In fact the output voltage is reduced by an amount which is equal to twice the bias potential. IC3 is a precision 1.26-volt reference generator, and together with VR2 it enables the output potential of the temperature sensor to be effectively reduced by anything from zero to 2.52 volts.

If, for example, a range of 0 to 100 degrees Centigrade is required, VR2 could be adjusted to reduce the sensor voltage by 2.33 volts so that an output of 0.4 volts is produced with the sensor at 0 degrees Centigrade. With an 8-bit analogue-to-digital converter designed to have an input voltage range of 0 to 2.55 volts, or 10 millivolts per division, a temperature range of 0 to 100 degrees would conveniently return values of 40 to 140 from the converter. Deducting 40 from the returned values would therefore give an answer in degrees Centigrade.

This gives a resolution of one degree Centigrade, but a higher level of performance can easily be obtained. By replacing R5 with a 200 k (1%) resistor the reduction in the sensor voltage would still be obtained, but IC1b would provide a voltage gain of two times. As a result of this the output-voltage range for temperatures of 0 to 100 degrees Centigrade would be boosted to 0.8 to 2.8 volts. The upper limit is too high for the converter, but using a higher voltage from VR2 would correct this. For instance, a 2.5-volt reduction in the output from the sensor would give a 0.46 to 2.46 voltage range, and this could be converted to reading in degrees Centigrade by deducting 46 and dividing by two. Again here, we are assuming that the analogue-to-digital converter is a type having a 2.55-volt full-scale sensitivity. With this system an improved resolution of 0.5 degrees Centigrade is obtained.

This basic arrangement can be used for other temperature ranges by adjusting VR2 for the appropriate offset, and using IC1b with a certain amount of voltage amplification where only a relatively restricted temperature range is needed. The voltage gain of IC1b is equal to the value of R5 divided by the value of R4.

Temperature Switch

Where a temperature sensor to drive a digital input is required the circuit of Figure 24 (which was described earlier) can be used. The only modification required is to replace photocell Tr1 with a thermistor. A VA1055S is suitable and enables a wide threshold temperature range to be accommodated.

Light Pen

An obvious omission so far in this chapter is a light-pen circuit. Light pen is perhaps a slightly misleading term since it gives the impression that it produces light, whereas it does in fact detect light. The basic idea is that the cathode ray tube of the television set or monitor is scanned by the electron beam, and this effectively gives a spot of light which is scanned in lines across the screen. The standard system has the first scan across the top of the screen, then a little lower, then lower still, until after several hundred scans the whole screen has been covered. In fact most systems use interlacing, where only every other line is scanned, then on the next run down the screen the lines that were missed the first time are scanned, then the original set of lines are scanned, and so on. The point of interlacing is that it gives a more stable and flicker-free picture.

Although the scanning process is too rapid for the human eye to perceive the process properly, a light-sensitive device such as a photo-Darlington placed against the screen can detect the spot of light as it passes, and send a signal to the computer. Many home-computers have a light-pen input these days, and it is usually to be found at the joystick port. The position of the light pen on the screen can be determined using software and a simple timing process, and again, many home-computers have some built-in hardware which makes this task relatively straightforward. It is usually just a matter of reading two registers of the CRT controller chip, the two readings giving the vertical and horizontal positions of the pen. With the position of the light pen detected, a software routine is used to turn on a small graphics block (or any desired screen character) at that location. Therefore, as the pen is moved across the screen a series of blocks or other characters are switched on, producing a line across the screen where the light pen has been. An important point to keep in mind is that a light pen cannot operate properly if a black background is selected, since there would obviously be no light spot to activate it. Of course, the system outlined above is just one way in which a light pen can be used, and there are numerous ways this type of equipment can be employed, both in games and in more serious applications.

A light pen is electrically quite simple. Integrated circuit light-activated switches that are suitable for this application and require only a minimum of discrete components are produced, but tend to be difficult to obtain, and expensive if you do! However, even a totaly discrete circuit is not very complex, and a suitable design is shown in the circuit

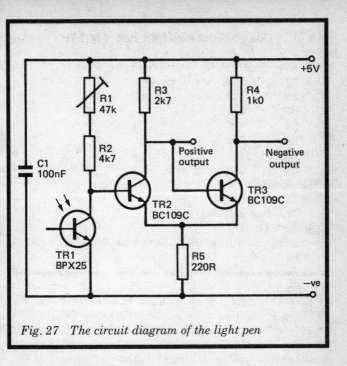

Fig. 27 The circuit diagram of the light pen

diagram of Figure 27.

The light sensor used in this circuit is a BPX25 photo-transistor, but any general-purpose phototransistor should be equally suitable. The high sensitivity of a photo-Darlington or cadmium sulphide photoresistor would be advantageous in this application, but neither of these are suitable as their response times are inadequate. High-speed photodiodes are often used in this application, but phototransistors have an adequate operating speed, and have the advantage of being relatively easy to obtain, inexpensive, and higher in sensitivity.

The circuit is really just a simple Schmitt trigger based on Tr2 and Tr3, with the input fed from the potential divider formed by Tr1 and R1 plus R2. When Tr1 receives the light pulse it switches on and takes the input of the Schmitt trig-

Resistors, all 0.25 W   5% except R1
    R1   47 k   0.1 W preset
    R2   4k7
    R3   2k7
    R4   1 k
    R5   220 R
Capacitor
    C1   100 nF ceramic
Semiconductors
    Tr1   BPX25
    Tr2, Tr3   BC109C (2 off)
Miscellaneous
    Printed circuit board, tube to take Tr1, wire, solder,
    etc.

ger low. This gives a positive output pulse at the collector of
Tr2, and a negative pulse at the collector of Tr3. In most
cases it will be the positive pulse from Tr2 that is required.
The outputs of the circuit will drive normal MOS inputs
satisfactorily, and most light-pen strobe inputs are of this
type. A buffer stage might be needed in order to drive a TTL
input properly.

R1 is given any setting which gives satisfactory results.
The sensitivity of the circuit is quite good, but if necessary
the sensitivity could be boosted slightly by making R5 a
little lower in value.

It is advisable to mount Tr1 in a tube with a fairly narrow
opening for the device to look out of. Apart from making the
pen easy to hold and use, this also helps to narrow the angle
of view of Tr1, which might otherwise be excessive, although
this particular phototransistor has a built-in lens which
helps considerably in this respect. The BPX25 has a lug near
the emitter leadout wire which might get in the way when
mounting the device, but this lug can be carefully removed
or bent out of the way. In use the tip of the pen should be

placed as close as possible to the television screen in order to obtain optimum reliability.

CHAPTER 3

Power Control

A few power-control circuits are featured in BP130: *Micro Interfacing Circuits – Book 1*, but these are all simple on/off types using relays or solid-state switching devices. In this chapter we will consider a few power controllers for 12-volt DC motors (or any similar applications), and these all provide a variable output power. These circuits are aimed primarily at those who are interested in computer-controlled model railways and robotics, but no doubt they have many other uses. In most cases the circuits provide very precise control of the output power, but a very inexpensive circuit for non-critical applications is also given.

Unipolar Controller

Figure 28 shows the circuit diagram of a unipolar (single-polarity output) controller. This is very straightforward in operation, and it is really just a buffered operational amplifier (non-inverting mode) circuit.

In order to give variable power the computer must generate a controlled voltage, and this is achieved using a digital-to-analogue converter. As this topic is covered in the first book we will not consider this part of the circuit here, but it will be assumed that a ZN428-based circuit is used, and that it gives an output voltage range of 0 to 2.55 volts (the output voltage obtained directly at the output of the ZN428). This voltage is obviously too low to drive a 12-volt DC motor, and the available current is far too low as well. We therefore require a circuit that provides a certain amount of voltage amplification plus a large amount of current amplification.

In the circuit of Figure 28, IC1 is used to provide the voltage amplification and Tr1 is responsible for most of the current gain. R1 to R3 form a negative feedback network which

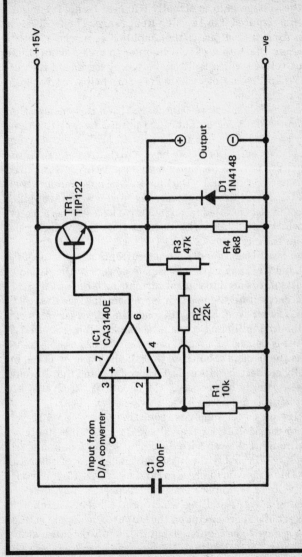

Fig. 28 A simple 12 volt DC power controller

sets the voltage gain of the circuit at the appropriate level, and the voltage gain is actually trimmed using Tr1 to produce the required 0 to 12-volt output range. The feedback is taken from the output of the amplifier as a whole, rather than from the output of IC1, in order to give a more stable output voltage which is little affected by loading of the output. When driving electric motors this helps to give good speed regulation.

R4 is merely a load resistor for Tr1, and this ensures that the emitter-follower output stage formed by Tr1 functions properly even if the circuit is used to drive a low-current load. It is essential for Tr1 to have a high-current gain if the circuit is to provide the fairly high output currents required in this application, and a Darlington type has therefore been used. D1 is used to suppress any high reverse-voltage spikes that could be generated by an inductive load such as a motor, and which could otherwise damage the semiconductor devices in the circuit.

The circuit can handle output currents of up to about 2 amps, but Tr1 may have to dissipate powers in the region of 15 watts if it is used to control currents as large as this. This would necessitate the use of a large heatsink such as a 2.6-degree C/watt type. Even with loads that draw currents of a few hundred milliamps a small heatsink will be required. If the unit is housed in a metal case it might be possible to use this as the heatsink, but note that the heat tab of Tr1 is internally connected to its collector terminal, and that it would almost certainly be necessary to insulate Tr1 from the case or heatsink using normal plastic washer and bush.

A 15-volt power supply is required, rather than a 12-volt type, to compensate for the voltage drop that inevitably occurs through Tr1, even with the circuit set for maximum output voltage. Probably the most convenient way of obtaining a suitable supply is to use a circuit based on a 15-volt monolithic voltage regulator. This system has the advantage of providing current-limiting which protects the controller in the event of a short-circuit on the output. The supply voltage does not have to be regulated, but the supply potential at full load should not be less than 15 volts, and no more than a few

74

volts above this figure. This avoids problems with an inadequate output voltage or excessive dissipation in Tr1.

The easiest way of adjusting R3 is to start with this set for maximum resistance, and to write 255 to the digital-to-analogue converter so that it gives maximum output voltage. Backing off R3 will at some stage cause the voltage to fall from its initial value, and it should then be adjusted for increased resistance, but just far enough to return the output voltage to its maximum level again. The circuit does not have a zero adjustment-control as in most applications it will not matter whether or not the output drops right down to zero volts when 0 is written to the digital-to-analogue converter. However, if this should be important for some reason an offset-null control is easily added. The track of the 10 k preset potentiometer should be wired across pins 1 and 5 of IC1, and the wiper should be connected to the negative supply rail via a 4k7 resistor.

There is no built-in circuitry to enable the polarity of the output to be controlled, but this could be achieved using a DPDT relay driven from a latching output via a suitable driver circuit. Alternatively, a DPDT switch could be used to provide manual control of the output polarity.

Bipolar Controller

Figure 29 shows the circuit diagram of a bipolar power controller. With this type of circuit dual-balanced supplies are used so that the non-earthy output of the controller can be made positive or negative of the earth rail without using a relay or switch at the output. In a motor-control application this gives the ability to easily set the direction of the motor as well as its speed, and no latching digital output is needed. The theoretical number of speeds available is reduced from 255 plus off, to 127 in one direction and 128 in the other. Even given that in practice some of the low-output voltages will be unusable as they will not be sufficient to drive the motor, this still gives a number of speeds that are likely to be far more than adequate in practice.

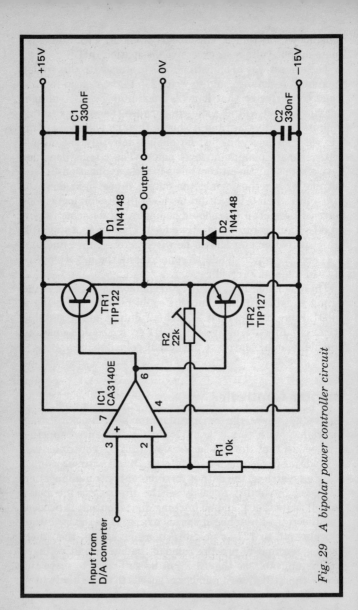

Fig. 29   A bipolar power controller circuit

The circuit is similar to a class B audio power amplifier. IC1 is used as the voltage-amplifier and driver stage while Tr1 and Tr2 form the complimentary class B emitter-follower output stage. The purpose of the latter is to give the circuit the required high-output current capability. Overall negative feedback is provided by R2 plus R1, and the voltage gain of the circuit can be controlled using R2. The circuit requires a nominal −5-volt to +5-volt input range, and R2 is adjusted to give the required −12-volt to +12-volt output voltage range.

In operation Tr1 acts as the output stage when the output is positive, and Tr2 is then cut off. When the output is negative it is Tr1 that is cut off and Tr2 acts as the emitter-follower output stage. Tr1 and Tr2 are both Darlington pair-power devices so that they can provide the high-current gains needed here, and can also handle the fairly high current and power levels involved in this application. D1 and D2 are used to suppress any high reverse-voltages that may be generated by the load.

This circuit can control output currents of up to 2 amps, but a large heatsink will be needed for both Tr1 and Tr2 if substantial output currents are to be handled. Otherwise, Tr1 and (or) Tr2 will overheat and be destroyed. Probably the easiest way of providing the dual-balanced 15-volt supplies is to use a circuit based on monolithic voltage regulators. These would provide current-limiting on both supply rails so that the controller would be fully protected against short-circuits or other overloads on the output. Stabilised supply rails are not essential, and they do not even have to be accurately balanced, but the minimum acceptable voltages are plus and minus 15 volts. Loaded supply potentials much above 15 volts are undesirable as this would result in an unnecessarily high dissipation in Tr1 and Tr2.

R2 is simply adjusted by trial and error to find the correct level of voltage gain that just takes the output fully positive or negative with the input voltage at its maximum and minimum levels.

Bipolar Converter

A slight problem with the bipolar-controller circuit of Figure 29 is that it requires a bipolar input voltage. A normal digital-to-analogue converter provides a unilateral output of typically 0 to 2.55 volts, or perhaps something like 0 to 5 or 0 to 10 volts when an output buffer/amplifier has beeen added. Fortunately it is quite easy to produce a bipolar signal from a unipolar input, and Figure 30 shows a simple circuit to achieve this. The circuit requires an input of 0 to 2.55 volts, plus a 2.55-volt reference voltage. A ZN428 digital-to-analogue converter provides both of these.

The circuit is actually very similar to the normal digital-to-analogue converter output buffer/amplifier, but in this case a negative supply for the operational amplifier (IC1) is

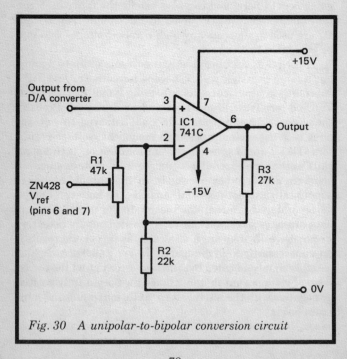

Fig. 30   A unipolar-to-bipolar conversion circuit

obviously mandatory, since the output of IC1 has to swing negative of the earth rail.

In order to take the voltage down below the earth rail when the output voltage from the converter is less than half its maximum figure, R1 is used to provide a positive bias to the inverting input of IC1. R1 is actually a preset resistor, and it is adjusted by empirical means to the point where the maximum positive and negative output voltages are equal (or at least within a few millivolts of being the same potential). R1 is fed from the precision voltage source of the ZN428 so that good stability is obtained, and frequent readjustment of R1 is not necessary. The values of R2 and R3 have been chosen to give approximately the required −5-volt to +5-volt output voltage swing. This does not need to be highly accurate since the voltage gain of the controller is adjustable, and it is R2 in the controller circuit that is used to set the overall gain of the system at a suitable level.

Pulsed Controller

For many applications a controller circuit of the type shown in Figure 28 (described earlier) is perfectly adequate, but if used as a motor controller it may have inadequate performance at low speeds. The problem is simply that at low speeds the amount of power being fed to the motor is quite low and only a small increase in the mechanical loading on the motor is likely to be sufficient to stall it. Another problem is that of poor starting performance, which is likely to be most noticeable in an application such as a model-train controller. Basically the problem is just that the motor needs more power to get started than it needs to keep operating once it has got under way. In practice this means that a fairly high power has to be applied to the motor before it will start, and once it has started it immediately jumps to a fairly high operating speed. This slow-speed stalling and jump- starting is something that will be familiar to anyone who has used an electric model railway with a simple train controller.

Although these problems may appear to be insurmountable, there are actually several ways of obtaining improved performance. Probably the best known of these, and the most simple one that is really effective, is the pulsed-controller type of circuit. With this type of controller the signal fed to the motor is not a straightforward DC one, but instead is a pulsed DC signal. Usually the pulse frequency is fixed, but the pulse width is variable. A short-pulse duration therefore gives only a very small average output voltage, and too little power is fed to the motor to activate it. On the other hand, if the pulse width is made so long that when one pulse ends the next one follows on almost at once, the average output voltage is almost equal to the supply potential, and the motor is driven at what can for all practical purposes be regarded as full power.

The point of this system is that the motor is driven at full power during the periods it receives pulses from the controller. These bursts of full power help to prevent stalling when the motor is operating at low speeds, and also tends to jolt it into operation and aid good starting performance.

The block diagram of Figure 31 shows the typical arrangement used in a pulsed controller. An oscillator operating at a low-to-middle frequency is used to drive a pulse-width modulator circuit. The latter is a form of monostable multivibrator, and it generates a pulse each time it is triggered by the oscillator. The pulse length can be varied by a control voltage, and therefore the average output voltage can be varied by means of a control voltage. This voltage is obtained from a digital-to-analogue converter via an amplifier which ensures that a suitably large control-voltage range is provided. Finally, a buffer stage at the output of a pulse-width modulator ensures that the circuit can provide the high current required by the load.

Figure 32 shows the circuit diagram of a pulsed controller. The clock oscillator and pulse-width modulator are both based on 555-timer devices (IC2 and IC3 respectively).

IC2 is used in the astable mode, but this circuit does not quite conform to the standard 555 astable configutation. What we require here is a circuit that provides very brief negative trigger pulses for the pulse-width modulator. With

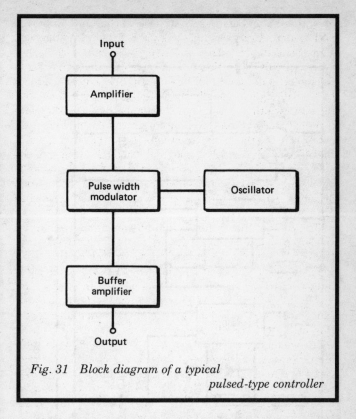

Fig. 31 Block diagram of a typical
pulsed-type controller

a 555 astable circuit the timing capacitor (C1) is first charged via two resistors (R4 and R5), and then discharged via one of these resistors (R5) and an internal transistor of the 555. The output at pin 3 goes high while the capacitor is charging and low while it is discharging. In this circuit steering diode D1 has been included so that R5 is bypassed when C1 is discharging, and a very short discharge time is consequently produced. This gives the required very short negative output duration.

IC3 is used in the standard 555 monostable configuration. It is triggered by applying a negative pulse to the trigger

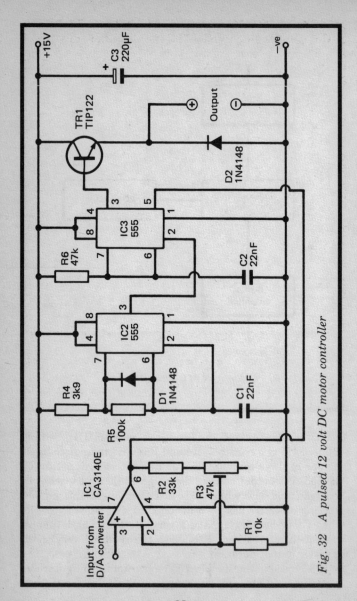

Fig. 32 A pulsed 12 volt DC motor controller

82

Components for Pulsed Motor Controller (Fig. 32)

Resistors, all 0.25 W   5% except R3
    R1   10 k
    R2   33 k
    R3   47 k   0.1 W preset
    R4   3k9
    R5   100 k
    R6   47 k
Capacitors
    C1, C2   22 nF polyester (2 off)
    C3   220 μF 25 V electrolytic
Semiconductors
    IC1   CA3140E
    IC2, IC3 555 (2 off)
    Tr1   TIP122
    D1, D2   1N4148 (2 off)
Miscellaneous
    Printed circuit board, heatsink for Tr1, insulating
    set for Tr1, output sockets, wire, solder, etc.

input at pin 2, and in this case pin 2 is simply coupled direct-ly to the output of IC2. When IC3 is triggered, the switching transistor which previously placed a short-circuit across C2 is switched off. C2 then charges by way of R6 until the charge potential equals two-thirds of the supply voltage. The switching transistor then discharges C2, and the positive output pulse from pin 3 of IC3 ends.

The C2 charge potential at which the output pulse is ter-minated is set by an internal potential divider of IC3, but this potential can be modified by applying a control voltage to pin 5 of IC3. By applying a higher voltage here the thres-hold voltage is increased, as is the duration of each output pulse, since it takes C2 longer to charge to this increased potential. Conversely, reducing the threshold voltage re-duces the threshold voltage and shortens the output pulses.

In order to give the sort of control range needed in this

application a control-voltage range of almost 0 to 15 volts is required. IC1 is therefore used to amplify the 0 to 2.55-volt output of a ZN428 digital-to-analogue converter to give a suitably large output voltage swing. In practice R3 is adjusted to give IC1 the correct voltage range, and this is a matter of finding by trial and error the lowest value that gives full control of the motor speed.

Tr1 is an emitter-follower output stage, and once again a Darlington device has been used here to ensure that adequate current amplification is obtained. The power requirements and output current capability are the same as for the unipolar controller described earlier. One difference worth noting is that the power dissipated in Tr1 is not very high even when driving a high-current load. The reason for this is that Tr1 is either cut off and dissipating no significant power, or it is switched hard on and dissipates only a moderate amount of power. Due to the switching action it spends only an insignificant amount of time between these two extremes where the power dissipation is high. A large heatsink is therefore not needed for Tr1, but it is still advisable to fit it with at least a small finned heatsink.

Simple Controller

The circuits described so far have all used a high-quality digital-to-analogue converter to provide the control voltage for the controller, but it is not essential to do this. For many applicatons the degree of control provided using this system is far greater than is really needed, and a system using a very basic digital-to-analogue converter will often suffice.

A simple controller circuit of this type appears in Figure 33. This is similar to the unipolar controller described at the beginning of this chapter, and the circuitry around IC1 and Tr1 is essentially the same. The main difference is the addition of a simple digital-to-analogue converter using the resistor and diode network (R1 to R6 plus D1 to D5). This simple 5-bit circuit does not provide very good accuracy, and the resolution is not very great either with just 31 different

84

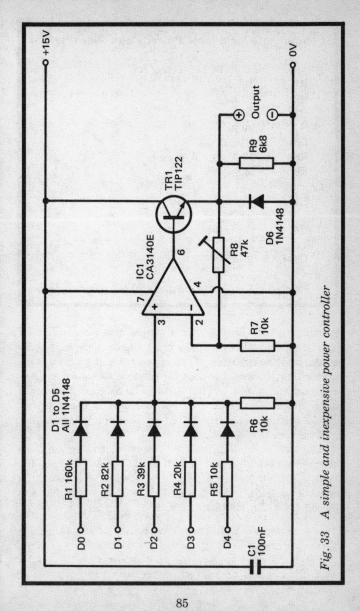

Fig. 33 A simple and inexpensive power controller

Components for Simple Power Controller (Fig. 33)

Resistors, all 0.25 W   5% except R8
R1	160 k
R2	82 k
R3	39 k
R4	20 k
R5–R7	10 k (3 off)
R8	47 k 0.1 W preset
R9	6k8

Capacitor
C1	100 nF ceramic

Semiconductors
IC1	CA3140E
Tr1	TIP122
D1–D6	1N4148 (6 off)

Miscellaneous
Printed circuit board, output sockets, wire, solder, etc

speeds plus off. However, for a simple motor controller for (say) a model railway a range of 31 speeds is perfectly adequate, and the accuracy of the converter is not very important either. It would in fact be possible to obtain greater accuracy and resolution, but it would be pointless to do so in most applications, and it is probably best to use a proper digital-to-analogue converter in applications where higher performance is essential.

The circuit should give good results if it is driven from any normal latching port (a 6821 or 8255 PIA, for example). With a little ingenuity it should be possible to successfully adopt a similar low-cost approach with the bipolar and pulsed-controller circuits.

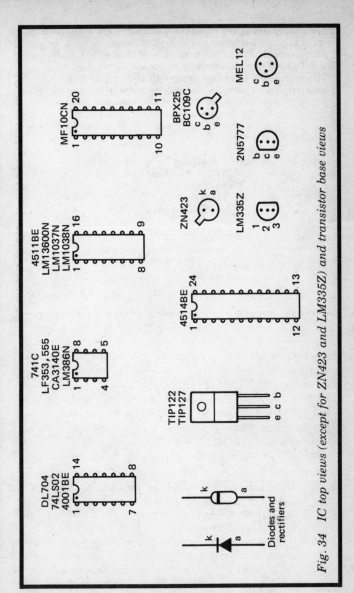

Fig. 34 IC top views (except for ZN423 and LM335Z) and transistor base views

87

Please note following is a list of other titles that are available in our range of Radio, Electronics and Computer Books.

These should be available from all good Booksellers, Radio Component Dealers and Mail Order Companies.

However, should you experience difficulty in obtaining any title in your area, then please write directly to the publisher enclosing payment to cover the cost of the book plus adequate postage.

If you would like a complete catalogue of our entire range of Radio, Electronics and Computer Books then please send a Stamped Addressed Envelope to:

BERNARD BABANI (publishing) LTD
THE GRAMPIANS
SHEPHERDS BUSH ROAD
LONDON W6 7NF
ENGLAND